The People of the State of New York

By the Grace of God, Free and Independent

represented in Senate and Assembly do enact as follows:

. . . It shall be the duty of the commission to initiate, formulate and execute plans, in cooperation and conjunction with the appropriate officers of the state education department and the state library therein, for the creation of a New York state freedom train to provide for the exhibition throughout the state of original documents, manuscripts and other historical materials preserved in the archives of the state library or in any other libraries or sources within or without the state, reflecting the traditions of liberty and freedom and the historical heritage of the people of the state . . .

Laws of 1948 Chapter 659. Enacted March 30, 1948.

NEW YORK STATE

FREEDOM TRAIN COMMISSION

GERALD H. SALISBURY, *Chairman*
Albany, New York

WALLACE A. BRENNAN, *Vice Chairman*
Dunkirk, New York

HARRY PRITCHARD TALCOTT
Brewster, New York

HERBERT C. CAMPBELL, *Dept. of Commerce*
Albany, New York

DR. CHARLES F. GOSNELL, *New York State Library*
Albany, New York

SENATOR HENRY W. GRIFFITH
Palmyra, New York

SENATOR THOMAS C. DESMOND
Newburgh, New York

SENATOR JAMES C. CRAWFORD
Brooklyn, New York

ASSEMBLYMAN ELMER J. KELLAM
Hancock, New York

ASSEMBLYMAN LOUIS A. CIOFFI
New York, New York

ASSEMBLYWOMAN MAUDE E. TEN EYCK
New York, New York

EX-OFFICIO MEMBERS

SENATOR ARTHUR H. WICKS,
Kingston, New York

SENATOR WALTER J. MAHONEY
Buffalo, New York

ASSEMBLYMAN OSWALD D. HECK
Schenectady, New York

ASSEMBLYMAN D. MALLORY STEPHENS
Brewster, New York

ASSEMBLYMAN LEE B. MAILLER
Cornwall-on-Hudson, New York

SENATOR ELMER F. QUINN
New York, New York

ASSEMBLYMAN IRWIN STEINGUT
Brooklyn, New York

OFFICIAL

Document Book

NEW YORK STATE

FREEDOM TRAIN

DISTRIBUTED BY

THE NEW YORK STATE LIBRARY
ALBANY, NEW YORK

1 9 5 0

TO THE READER...

It is fitting for us, in this day of many 'isms, to open a book which re-prints the precious documents that tell the March of Freedom in New York State.

The story these pages unfold is simple and sincere. The documents have been arranged so that you, the reader, may see how freedom — sometimes through trial and error, in violence and in peace — comes down to us as a living force in our everyday life.

The objective of the New York State Freedom Train is to provide a "university on wheels," which as it tours the State will give every student, and adult person, the opportunity to see and study firsthand the original documents of his heritage.

This official book is designed as a "primer" to aid this study; it reproduces faithfully the documents — some yellowed with age; others scarred by fire — as they are shown on the train, and identifies them with a few salient facts and dates. No effort has been made to editorialize or to give opinion. This right is reserved for the reader.

Gerald H. Salisbury

Chairman

NEW YORK STATE FREEDOM TRAIN COMMISSION

ACKNOWLEDGMENTS

All documents reproduced here are from the archives of the New York State Library in Albany, except for the ten listed below which were among those lent for exhibit on the New York State Freedom Train.

Those lent and reproduced are: Coxsackie Declaration of Independence — from the Albany Institute of History and Art, Albany; Pledge of Allegiance — from David Bellamy, Rochester; Charter of Liberties and Privileges — from Town of North Hempstead; Account Book, Southfield Town, Richmond County — from the Staten Island Historical Society, New York; Letter of Thomas Jefferson — from Washington Headquarters Commission, Newburgh; Antidiscrimination Law, 1948 — from Secretary of State, Albany; Duke's Laws — from Town of North Hempstead; Antidiscrimination Law, 1945 — from Secretary of State, Albany; John Jay Secures Loan of 20 Cannon — from Washington Headquarters Commission, Newburgh; The New Colossus by Emma Lazarus — from American-Jewish Historical Society, New York.

This book designed and produced by George Shapiro.

MANY of us take our basic freedoms for granted. This we should never do, for every right we possess today was won only after a long and sorely contested struggle.

The priceless documents you see displayed on your New York State Freedom Train, and the principles of liberty for which they stand, are related one to another, like father to son. Though some are in Dutch, others in early English — each hands down its message so that every generation, including ours, may enjoy these privileges.

We must remember, as well, that every right is accompanied by a responsibility. We cannot be good citizens by merely accepting freedom; we must do our duty each day as free citizens. This is the simple lesson we so humbly learn as we look upon and study these documents. Surely, as we leave the Freedom Train, imbued with this spirit, we know that freedom is our most priceless possession and we owe it our highest duty.

GOVERNOR.

The New York State Freedom Train, which toured the
State from January 1949 to February 1950, was an impressive
library on wheels to all of the communities visited. It
brought to them the realization that the liberty and the
freedoms which we all enjoy today are living fulfillments of
our nation's and our State's purposes and laws. The eighty-
four carefully selected documents aboard the Train, all except
ten from the archives of the New York State Library, explained
the meaning of our cultural heritage of freedom in terms of
its origin and emphasized its continuity. We gathered that
the American Way of Life so well expressed in the historical
development of our State is in essence the advancement of the
general will through limited controversy contained within the
framework of Constitution and laws making for the ready adjust-
ments of the needs, desires, and aspirations of all our people
despite their variegated origins.

To this share in the planning and participation of the
New York State Freedom Train the State Education Department and
the New York State Library were proud contributors. For it is
in the education of the people to the ways of freedom that we
are both dedicated in purpose and by law. The Official Document
Book will be a reminder of our mission during the past year and
shall ever be immortalized by printed page for generations of
school children and college students to know and to learn.

Let us always remember in the language of our forefathers the source of our richness of cultural heritage: "We,
the People of the State of New York, by Grace of God, Free and
Independent!"

Acting Commissioner

THE NEW COLOSSUS * By EMMA LAZARUS

Not like the giant of Greek fame,
With conquering limbs astride from land to land;
Here at our sea-washed, sunset gates shall stand
A mighty woman with a torch, whose flame
Is the imprisoned lightning, and her name
Mother of Exiles. From her beacon-hand
Glows world-wide welcome; her mild eyes command
The air-bridged harbor that twin cities frame.

"Keep, ancient lands, your storied pomp!" cries she
With silent lips. "Give me your tired, your poor,
Your huddled masses yearning to breathe free,
The wretched refuse of your teeming shore.
Send these, the homeless, tempest-tost to me,
I lift my lamp beside the golden door!"

* Original manuscript displayed on
New York State Freedom Train.

CONTENTS

Government By The People...

To give the people a voice in the government, James, Duke of York, proclaimed in his famous CHARTER OF LIBERTIES AND PRIVILEGES, 1683, that . . . *"the supreme legislative authority shall reside in a Governor, Council and the people met in General Assembly."*

The Charter of Libertyes and privileidges graunted by his Royall Highnesse to the Inhabitants of New Yorke and its Dependencyes.

FFor the better Establishing the Governement of this Province of New Yorke and that Justice and right may be Equally done to all persons within the same

BEE It Enacted by the Governour Councell and Representatives now in Generall Assembly mett and assembled and by the authority of the same,

THat The Supreame Legislative Authority under his Majesty and Royall Heighnesse James Duke of Yorke Albany &c Lord Proprietor of the said Province Shall forever be and reside in a Governour, Councell, and the people mett in Generall Assembly.

THat The Exercise of the Cheife Magistracy and Administraçon of the Governement over the said Province Shall bee in the said Governour assisted in a Councell with whose advice and Consent or with at least four of them he is to rule and Governe the same according to the Lawes thereof.

THat In Case the Governour Shall dye or be absent out of the Province and that there be noe person within the said Province Comissionated or appointed by his Royall Highnesse his heires or Successours to be Governour or Comander in Cheife there That then the Councell for the time being or soe many of them as are in the said Province doe take upon them the Administraçon of the Governour and the Execuçon of the Lawes thereof and powers and authorityes belonging to the Governour and Councell The first in nominaçon in which Councell is to preside untill the said Governour Shall returne and arrive in the said Province againe, or the pleasure of his Royall Highnesse his heires or Successours Shall be further knowne.

THat According to the usage Custome and practice of the Realme of England a sessions of a Generall Assembly be held in this Province once in three yeares at least.

THat Every ffreeholder within this Province and ffreeman in any Corpora

Government By The People...

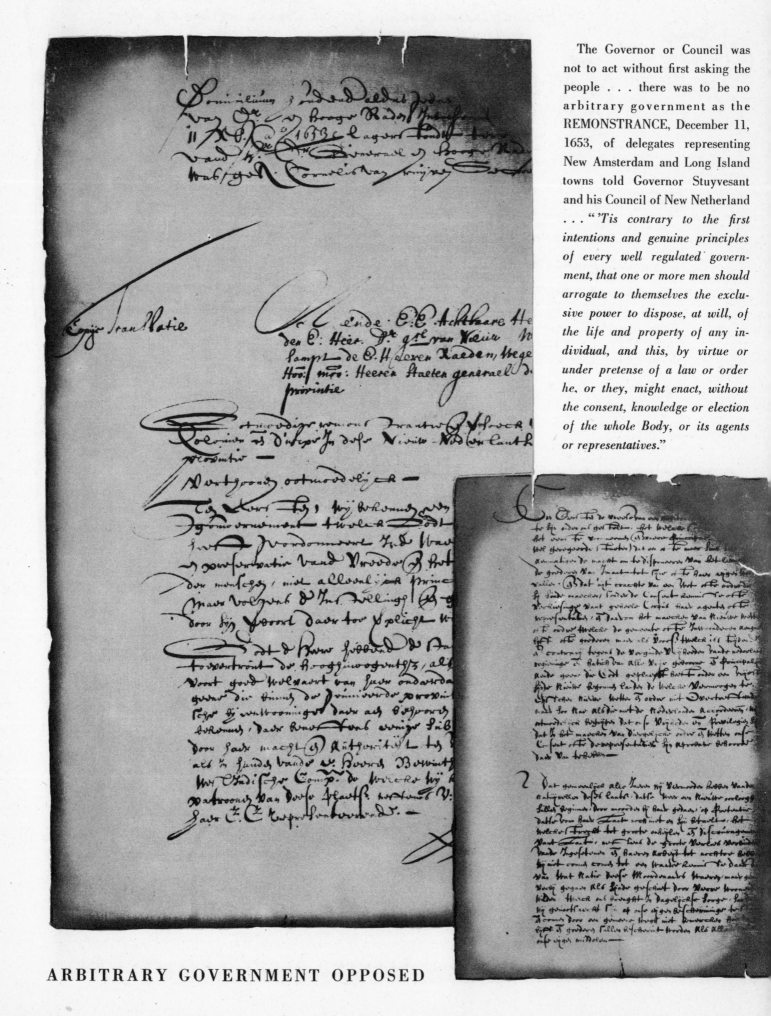

The Governor or Council was not to act without first asking the people . . . there was to be no arbitrary government as the REMONSTRANCE, December 11, 1653, of delegates representing New Amsterdam and Long Island towns told Governor Stuyvesant and his Council of New Netherland . . . *"'Tis contrary to the first intentions and genuine principles of every well regulated government, that one or more men should arrogate to themselves the exclusive power to dispose, at will, of the life and property of any individual, and this, by virtue or under pretense of a law or order he, or they, might enact, without the consent, knowledge or election of the whole Body, or its agents or representatives."*

ARBITRARY GOVERNMENT OPPOSED

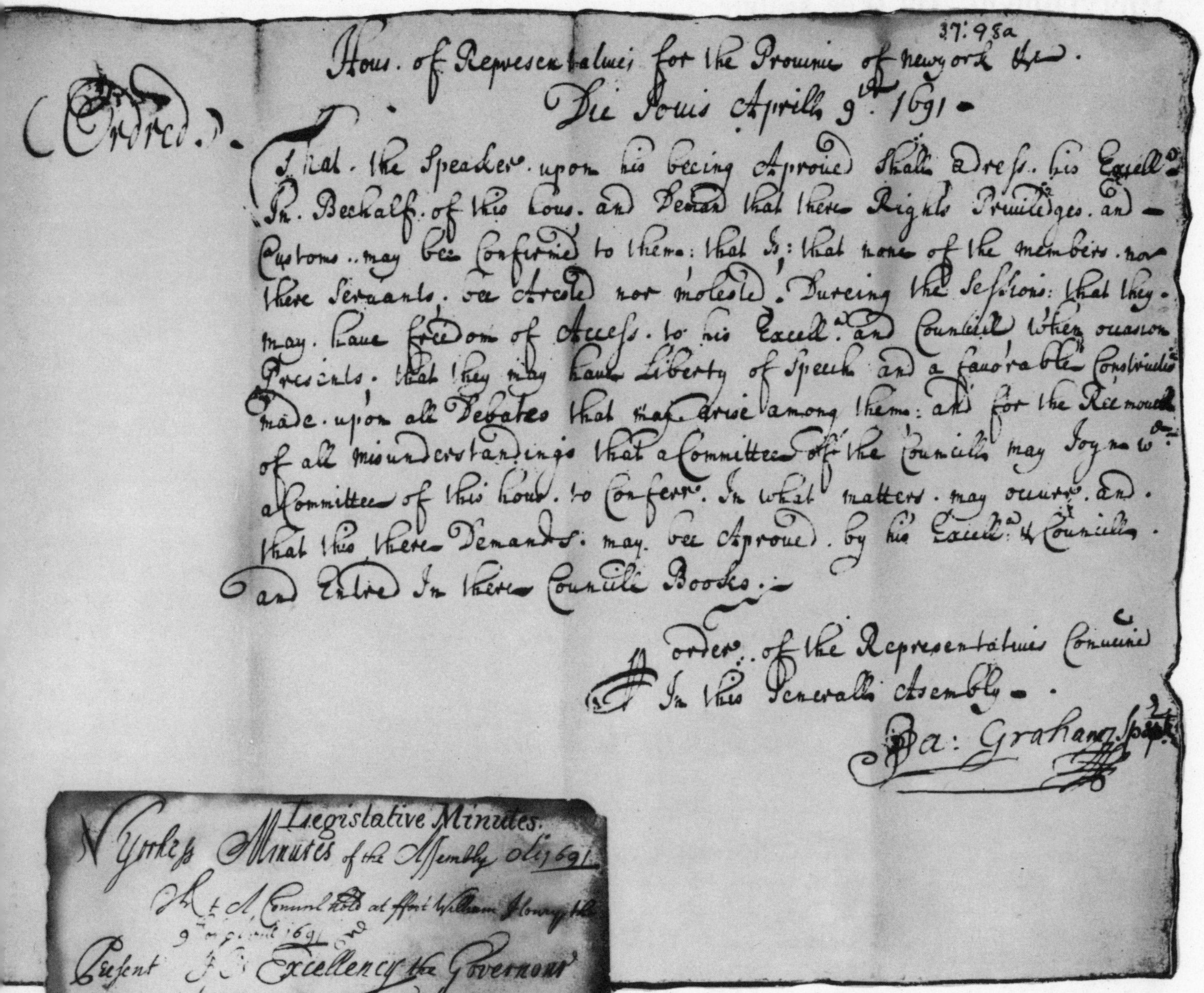

House of Representatives for the Province of new york the

Die Jovis Aprills 9th 1691

Ordered.

That the Speaker upon his beeing Aproved shall address his Excell.
In Behalf of this hous and Demand that there Rights Priviledges and
Customs may bee Confirmed to them: that is: that none of the members nor
there Servants bee Arested nor molested Dureing the sessions: that they
may have freedom of Access to his Excell. and Councell when occasion
presents, that they may have Liberty of Speech and a favorable Construction
made upon all Debates that may arise among them: and for the Reemoveall
of all misunderstandings that a Committee of the Councill may Joyne wth.
a Committee of this hous to Conferr In what matters may occur and
that this there Demands may bee Aproved by his Excell. & Councill.
and Entred In there Councill Books.

By order of the Representatives Convened
In this Generall Assembly.

Ja: Graham Spkr.

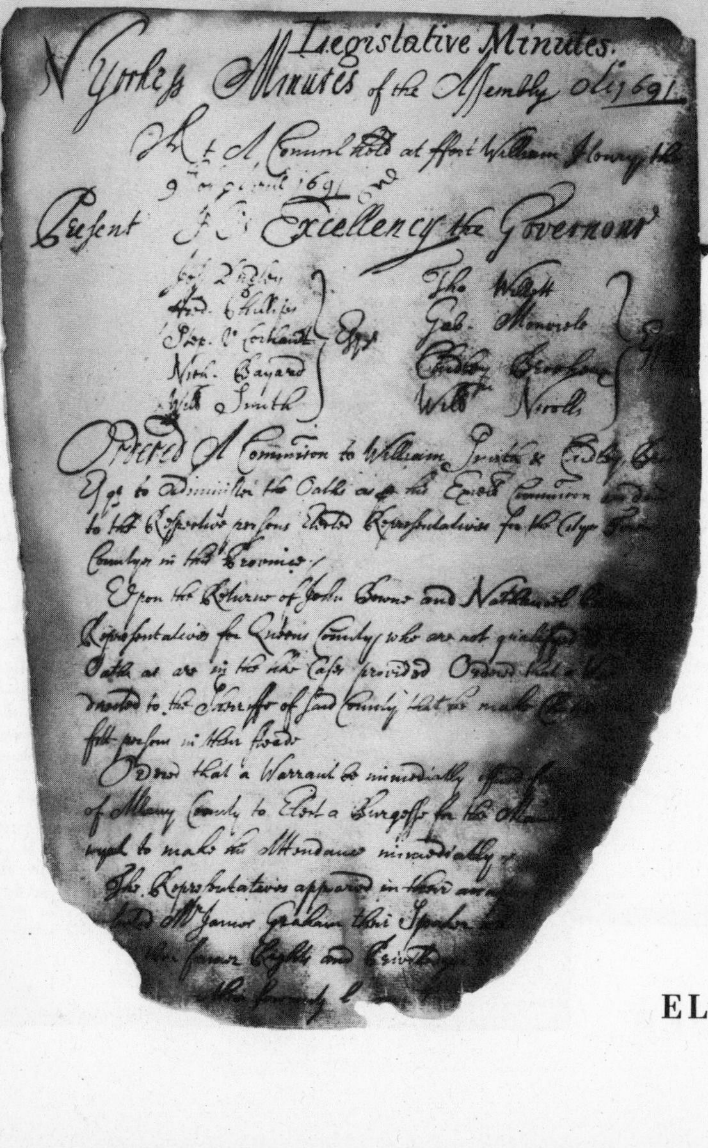

Shown at left is the title page from the MINUTES of New York's first Colonial Legislature, which assembled April 9, 1691. This legislature was made up of a Council and a House of Representatives, which was elected by the people and is now called the Assembly.

To insure that their voice be heard, and that their representatives be protected, the House in an ORDER, signed April 9, 1691, stated that Speaker James Graham . . . "address his Excellency in behalf of this house, and demand that there Rights Privileges and Customs may be Confirmed to them; that none of the members, nor there Servants; be arrested nor molested. . . ."

ELECTED REPRESENTATIVES MEET

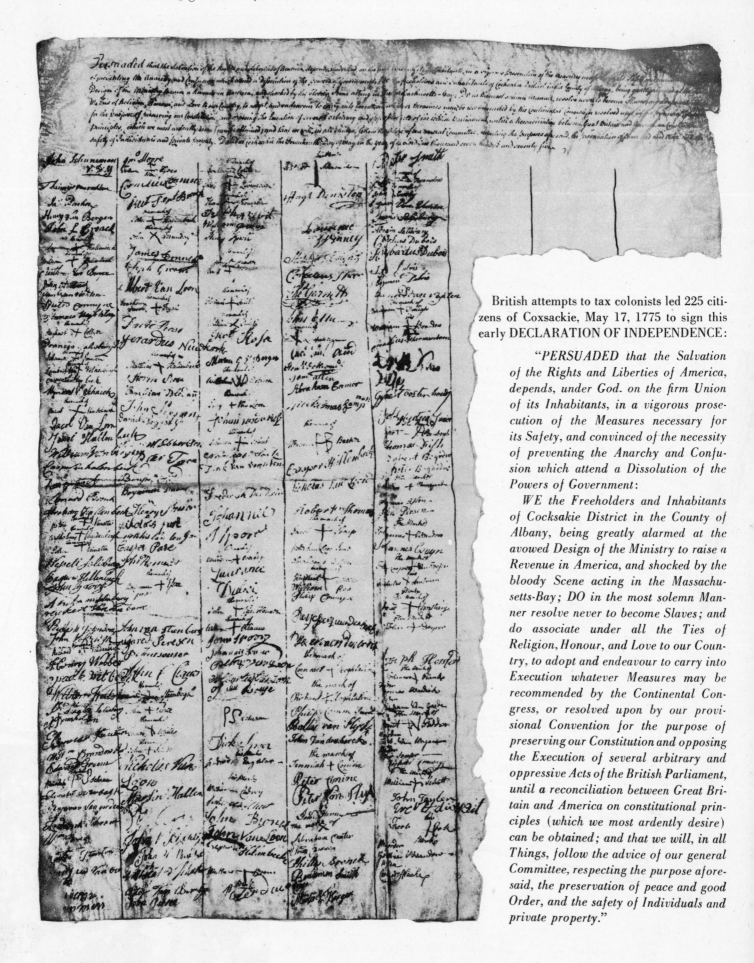

British attempts to tax colonists led 225 citizens of Coxsackie, May 17, 1775 to sign this early DECLARATION OF INDEPENDENCE:

"*PERSUADED that the Salvation of the Rights and Liberties of America, depends, under God. on the firm Union of its Inhabitants, in a vigorous prosecution of the Measures necessary for its Safety, and convinced of the necessity of preventing the Anarchy and Confusion which attend a Dissolution of the Powers of Government:*

WE the Freeholders and Inhabitants of Cocksakie District in the County of Albany, being greatly alarmed at the avowed Design of the Ministry to raise a Revenue in America, and shocked by the bloody Scene acting in the Massachusetts-Bay; DO in the most solemn Manner resolve never to become Slaves; and do associate under all the Ties of Religion, Honour, and Love to our Country, to adopt and endeavour to carry into Execution whatever Measures may be recommended by the Continental Congress, or resolved upon by our provisional Convention for the purpose of preserving our Constitution and opposing the Execution of several arbitrary and oppressive Acts of the British Parliament, until a reconciliation between Great Britain and America on constitutional principles (which we most ardently desire) can be obtained; and that we will, in all Things, follow the advice of our general Committee, respecting the purpose aforesaid, the preservation of peace and good Order, and the safety of Individuals and private property."

INDEPENDENCE SUPPORTED

Similar declarations were read in other towns. In Albany, MINUTES OF
THE COMMITTEE OF CORRESPONDENCE show that the Declaration of
Independence was read July 19, 1776 at the City Hall... *"to a large concourse
of the Inhabitants of the City and the Continental Troops in this City and
received with applause and satisfaction."*

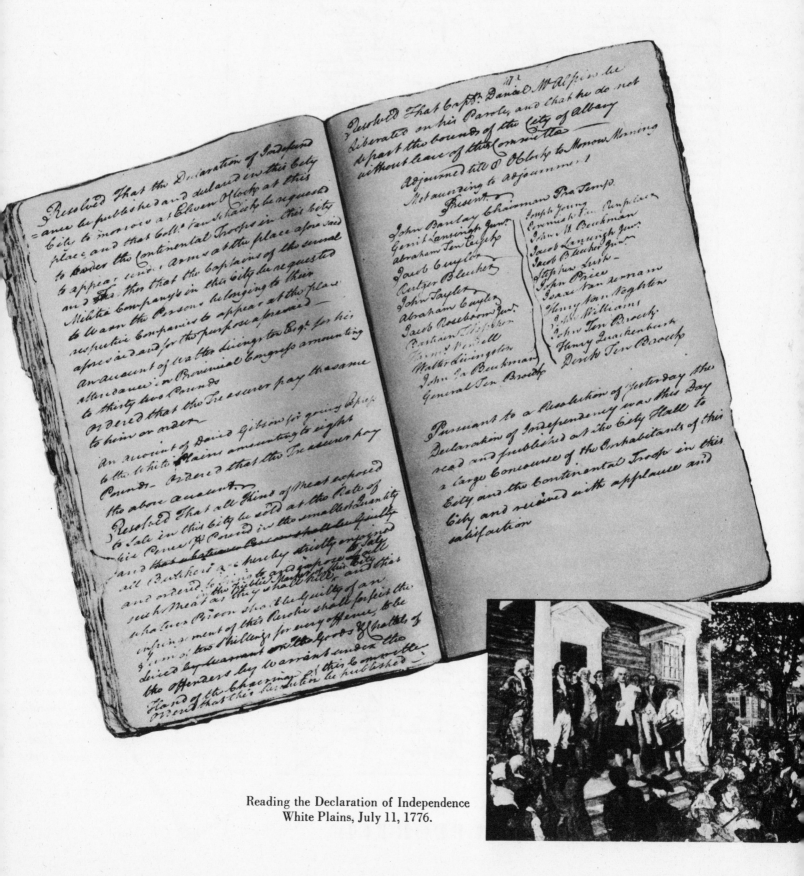

Reading the Declaration of Independence
White Plains, July 11, 1776.

Government By The People...

The people, through their elected Assembly, said real and personal property might be taxed to pay War and State debts. EARLY ASSESSMENT ROLLS for Livingston Manor and Cambridge District list the value of a man's real estate and the tax he must pay.

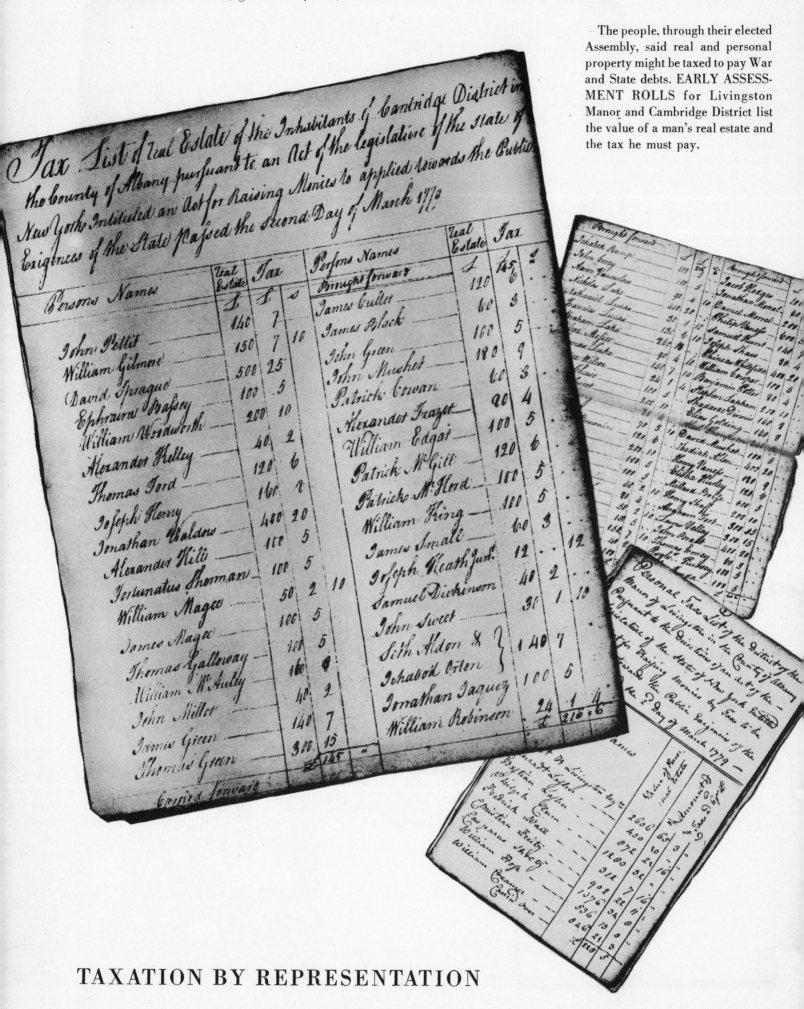

TAXATION BY REPRESENTATION

Private property was also to be protected. The Assembly, October 24, 1700, in a BILL TO PREVENT OPPRESSION, declared null and void a New York City ordinance which would tax flour and biscuit brought into the City. This bill was not approved by Governor and Council.

The Assembly called the ordinance..."an infringing and destruction of the libertys, propertys and inheritance of His Majesty's Subjects."

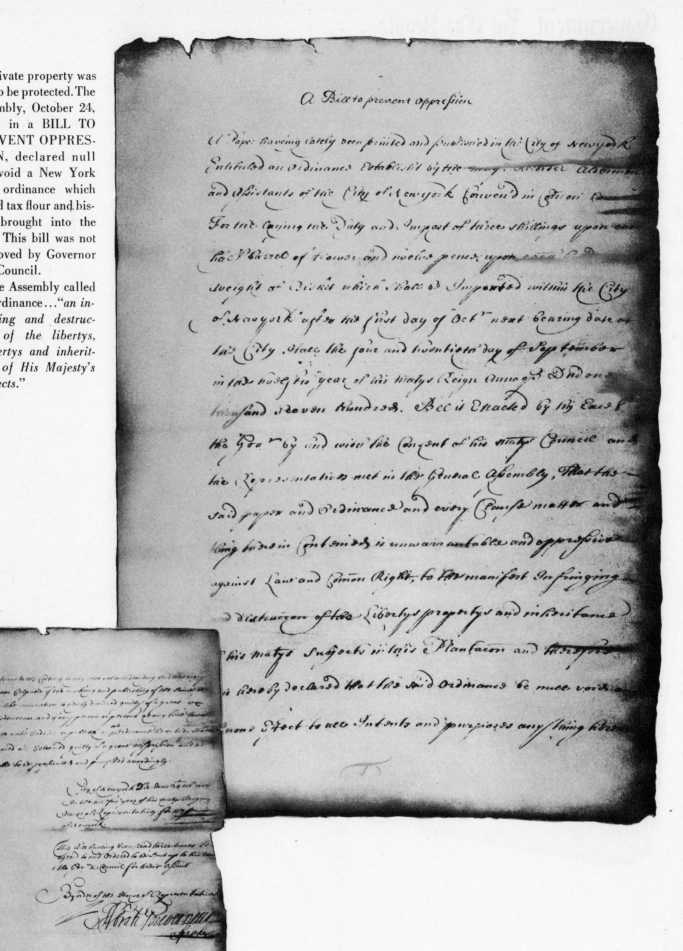

PRIVATE PROPERTY PROTECTED

therefore be silent upon so momentuous a Point, tho' we were not favoured with your Sentiments or Instructions; nor informed of what, or whether any thing had passed between you and the General respecting the disaffected Inhabitants. We look up the Subject on general Principles. There can be no Liberty where the military is not subordinate to the civil power, in every thing not immediately connected with their Operations. Your House the natural and proper Tribunal for all civil matters within the Circle of your own Jurisdiction was assembled; and Congress itself within the General's reach, ready to enforce every reasonable Proposition for the publick safety. To one or other he ought to have applied. A similar Effort in Rhode Island had passed over unredressed; reiterated Precedents must become dangerous: we therefore conceived it to be our unquestionable Duty to assert The

Independance and Superiority of the civil power, and to call the attention of Congress to this unwarrantable Increase of their Rights, big with one of their Officers. A Resolution passed, in consequence, on the 8th of March, that no Oath by way of Test be imposed upon, exacted or required of any Inhabitant of these Colonies by any military Officer — and it was ordered to be immediately published. We flatter ourselves that our Conduct on this Occasion will meet with your Approbation. This will be presented by Brigad General Thompson who for the present will command in your Capital; General Schuyler's Residence at Albany being deemed indispensable. General Thompson is a gallant Officer and very much respected in this Province; and we doubt not of your Endeavours to make his Command as agreeable to himself and as Salutary

Suggested it is best vacant untill he can have an Opportunity of being heard; of which you will be pleased to inform him.

We have the Honour to be with the utmost Regard

Gentlemen

Your most obedient humble Servants

Jas. Duane
Jno Jay
John Alsop
Lewis Morris

Philad. 1st March 1776

Be pleased to turn over

Our forefathers did not believe a country could remain free if the military dominated the civil branch of government. When General Charles Lee tried to impose a loyalty test on people of New York, Duane, Jay, Alsop and Morris, as delegates to the Continental Congress, protested, warning the New York Provincial Convention..."*There can be no liberty where the military is not subordinate to the civil power.*"

CIVIL SUPERIOR TO MILITARY POWER

United States, as nearly as may be. Every county heretofore established and separately organized, shall always be entitled to one member of the assembly; and no new county shall hereafter be erected, unless its population shall entitle it to a member.

Section 8. Any bill may originate in either house of the legislature and all bills passed by one house, may be amended by the other.

Section 9. The members of the legislature shall receive for their services a compensation, to be ascertained by law, and paid out of the public treasury; but no increase of the compensation shall take effect during the year in which it shall have been made. And no law shall be passed increasing the compensation of the members of the legislature, beyond the sum of three dollars a day.

Section 10. No member of the legislature shall receive any civil appointment from the governor and senate, or from the legislature, during the term for which he shall have been elected.

Section 11. No person being a member of congress, or holding any judicial or military office under the United States, shall hold a seat in the legislature. And if any person shall, while a member of the legislature, be elected to congress, or appointed to any office, civil or military, under the government of the United States, his acceptance thereof shall vacate his seat.

Section 12. Every bill, which shall have passed the senate and assembly, shall, before it become a law, be presented to the governor; if he approve, he shall sign it; but if not, he shall return it with his objections to that house in which it shall have originated; who shall enter the objections at large on their journal, and proceed to reconsider it. If after such reconsideration, two thirds of the members present shall agree to pass the bill, it shall be sent together with the objections to the other house, by which it shall likewise be reconsidered; and if approved by two thirds of the members present, it shall become a law. But in all such cases, the votes of both houses shall be determined by yeas and nays; and the names of the persons voting for and against the bill, shall be entered on the journal of each house, respectively. If any bill shall not be returned by the governor, within ten days (Sundays excepted) after it shall have been presented to him, the same shall be a law in like manner as if he had signed it, unless the legislature shall by their adjournment prevent its return, in which case it shall not be a law.

Section 13. All officers holding their offices during good behavior may be removed by joint resolution of the two houses of the legislature, if two

And the voice of the people, met in Assembly, was to control even the executive branch. Article 1, Section 12 of the 1821 CONSTITUTION, abolishing an early Council of Revision, provided for a veto by the Governor, but it could be over-ridden by a two-thirds vote of the Legislature.

LEGISLATION BY REPRESENTATION

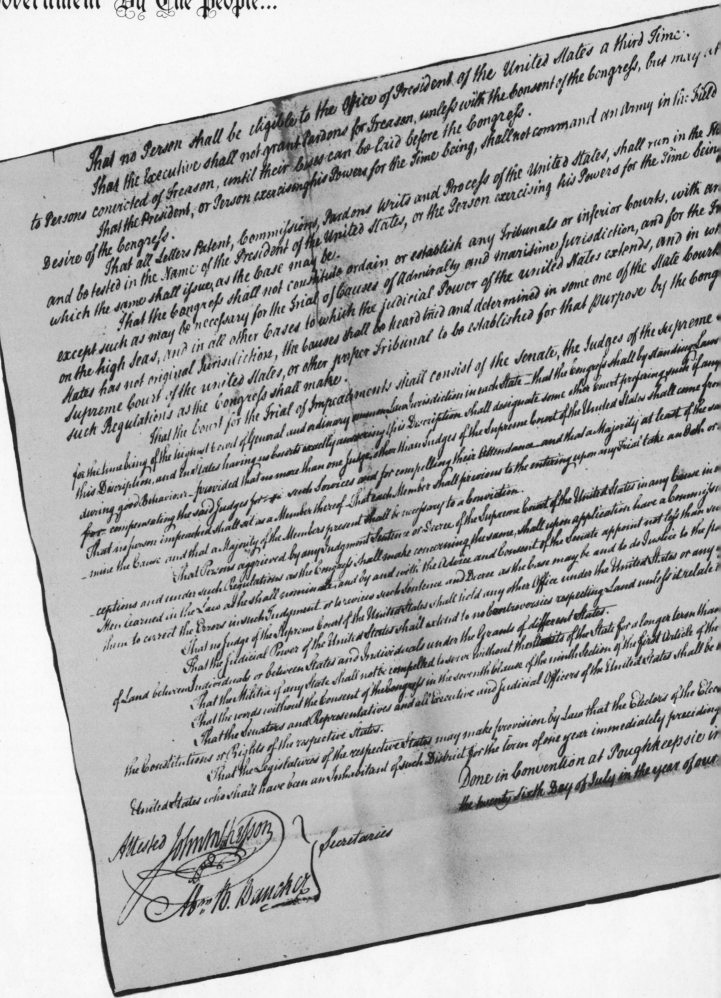

That no Person shall be eligible to the Office of President of the United States a third Time.

That the Executive shall not grant Pardons for Treason, unless with the Consent of the Congress, but may at...

to Persons convicted of Treason, until their Cases can be laid before the Congress.

That the President, or Person exercising his Powers for the Time being, shall not command an Army in the Field...

Desire of the Congress.

That all Letters Patent, Commissions, Pardons, Writs and Process of the United States, shall run in the Na...

and be tested in the Name of the President of the United States, or the Person exercising his Powers for the Time being...

which the same shall issue, as the Case may be.

That the Congress shall not constitute ordain or establish any Tribunals or inferior Courts, with...

except such as may be necessary for the Trial of Causes of Admiralty and maritime Jurisdiction, and for the...

on the high Seas; and in all other Cases to which the Judicial Power of the United States extends, and in wh...

States has not original Jurisdiction, the Causes shall be heard tried and determined in some one of the State Court...

Supreme Court of the United States, or other proper Tribunal to be established for that Purpose by the Cong...

such Regulations as the Congress shall make.

That the Court for the Trial of Impeachments shall consist of the Senate, the Judges of the Supreme...

for the time being of the highest Court of General and ordinary common Law Jurisdiction in each State — That the Congress shall by standing Laws...

this Description, and in States having no Courts exactly answering this Description shall designate some other Court preferring such if any...

during good Behaviour — provided that no more than one Judge, other than Judges of the Supreme Court of the United States shall come from...

for compensating the said Judges for such Services used for compelling their attendance — and that a Majority at least of the sa...

That no Person impeached shall act as a Member thereof. That each Member shall previous to the entering upon any Trial take an Oath or...

mine the Cause and that a Majority of the Members present shall be necessary to a Conviction.

That Persons aggrieved by any Judgment Sentence or Decree of the Supreme Court of the United States in any Cause in...

ceptions and under such Regulations as the Congress shall make concerning the same, shall upon application have a Commission...

Men learned in the Law as he shall nominate, and by and with the Advice and Consent of the Senate appoint not less than se...

them to correct the Errors in such Judgment, or to review such Sentence and Decree as the Case may be and to do Justice to the pa...

That no Judge of the Supreme Court of the United States shall hold any other Office under the United States or any...

That the Judicial Power of the United States shall extend to no Controversies respecting Land unless it relate...

of Land between Individuals or between States and Individuals under the Grants of different States.

That the Militia of any State shall not be compelled to serve without the Limits of the State for a longer term than...

That the Lands without the Consent of the Congress in the seventh Clause of the ninth Section of the first Article of the...

That the Senators and Representatives and all Executive and Judicial Officers of the United States shall be...

the Constitutions or Rights of the respective States.

That the Legislatures of the respective States may make provision by Law that the Electors of the Elec...

United States who shall have been an Inhabitant of such District for the term of one year immediately preceding...

Done in Convention at Poughkeepsie in...

the twenty Sixth Day of July in the year of our...

Attested John Anthepson } Secretaries

Abm W. Banchor

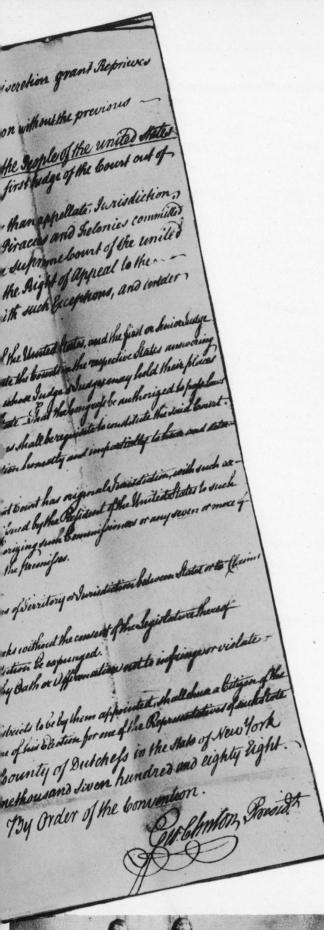

NEW YORK RATIFIES
CONSTITUTION
OF THE
UNITED STATES

New York ratified the Federal Constitution at Poughkeepsie, July 26, 1788. Thirty-three amendments were suggested, as signed by Governor George Clinton, President of the Convention. While these were not officially accepted for inclusion in the United States Constitution, they did form the basis for the first ten amendments, adopted in 1791 and known as the Bill of Rights.

Below, reproduction of the mural painting by Gerald Foster in the post office at Poughkeepsie, depicts the closing moments of the New York State ratifying convention. The delegates are, left to right: Philip Van Cortlandt, Cornelius Schoonmaker, Peter Vrooman, John Haring, Israel Thompson, Chancellor Robert R. Livingston, Melancton Smith, Governor George Clinton, Alexander Hamilton, Abraham Bancker, John Jay, James Clinton, Isaac Roosevelt, John Sloss Hobart, Jacobus Swartout, Peter Vandervoort, James Duane, Philip Livingston, John Lansing, Lewis Morris, Richard Morris, Dirck Wyncoop, Gozen Ryerss.

Government By The People...

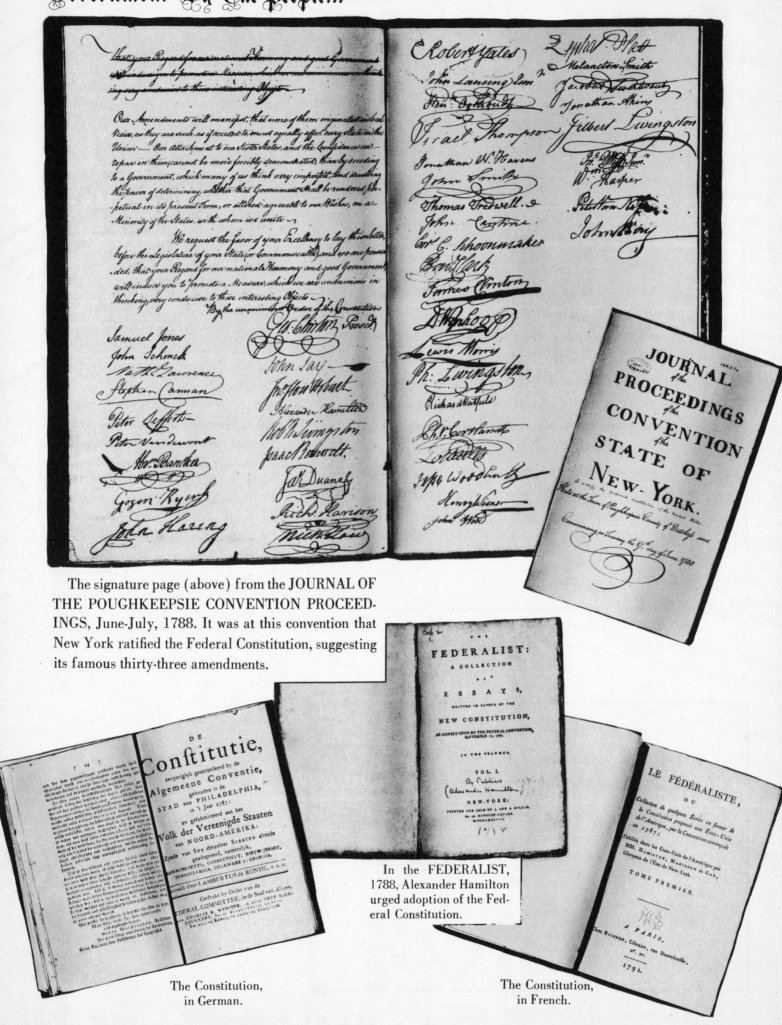

The signature page (above) from the JOURNAL OF THE POUGHKEEPSIE CONVENTION PROCEEDINGS, June-July, 1788. It was at this convention that New York ratified the Federal Constitution, suggesting its famous thirty-three amendments.

In the FEDERALIST, 1788, Alexander Hamilton urged adoption of the Federal Constitution.

The Constitution, in German.

The Constitution, in French.

WHITE HOUSE,
WASHINGTON.

December 17, 1901.

My dear Mr. Hale:

I value Mr. Cummings' sermon. If you meet him I wish you would tell him so. I thank you for sending it to me.

The great difficulty that I find is not to do harm to our brother by pretending to help him. The easy thing to do in international matters, for instance, is to follow those amiable but very far from wise philanthropists who think we can help our brother by doing nothing whatever, who think, for example, that we can benefit the Filipino by getting out of the Philippines and letting him wallow back into savagery. Unfortunately, the most difficult task is that which has been so conscientiously undertaken by Root and Taft, trying to bring the Filipinos forward in the path of orderly self-governing liberty.

Again, in South America it is positively difficult to know just how far it is best to leave the nations alone and how far there must be interference, and also how far we can with justice prevent interference by others; because in each case the equities vary.

Faithfully yours,

Theodore Roosevelt

And the principle of government by the people was applied by President Theodore Roosevelt in a letter to Rev. Edward E. Hale, December 17, 1901, saying . . . *"orderly self-governing liberty"* should be given the Philippines. Forty-five years later, President Harry S. Truman by Proclamation, July 4, 1946, which included the phrase...*"Whereas the people of the Philippines have clearly demonstrated their capacity for self-government,"* . . . granted the Filipinos "government by the people."

I pledge allegiance to my Flag and (to) the Republic for which it stands — one Nation indivisible — with liberty and justice for all,

Original draft of the PLEDGE OF ALLEGIANCE to the Flag, written in 1892 by Francis Bellamy. The Pledge was used for the first time, Columbus Day, 1892.

Freedom of

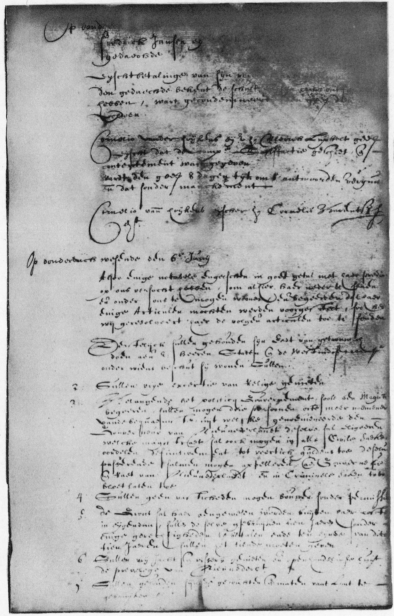

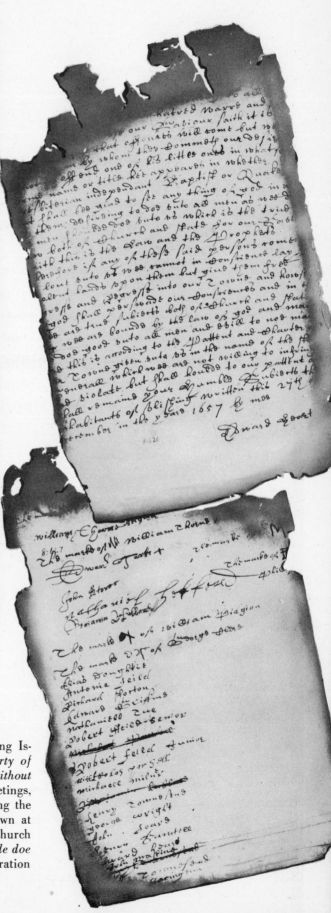

The free exercise of religion was among the privileges granted June 6, 1641 to Englishmen who were permitted by the Dutch West India Company's Director and Council to settle in New Netherland.

Because Governor Peter Stuyvesant violated Flushing, Long Island's Charter of 1645, which guaranteed settlers . . . *Liberty of Conscience, according to the custome and manner of Holland, without molestation or disturbance,* by forbidding Quakers to hold meetings, 26 freeholders (men of every religion) rose in protest, signing the FLUSHING REMONSTRANCE, two pages of which are shown at right, December 27, 1657. They said the true law both of Church and State is . . . *doe unto all men as wee desire all men shoulde doe unto us.* It has often been called . . . "America's first Declaration of Independence."

Religion...

The Quakers suffered for 6 years under Stuyvesant until John Bowne — who had been jailed for holding religious services in his home — was banished to Holland. There, the Directors of the West India Company released Bowne, telling Stuyvesant in the above CENSURE, April 16, 1663 to . . . *"at least not force people's consciences, but allow everyone to have his own belief, as long as he behaves quietly and legally, gives no offence to his neighbor and does not oppose the government."*

Governor Anthony Colve granted the Lutheran congregation in Albany free exercise of their religion, September 26, 1673.

Freedom of Religion...

[Handwritten document, left:]

Convention doth further in the Name and by —
the Authority of the Good People of this State
Ordain determine and declare that the
free Exercise & Enjoyment Toleration of Religeous Profession and
Worship without discrimination or preference, shall forever hereafter be allowed —
within this State to all mankind. Provided
that the Liberty of Conscience hereby Granted
shall not be so Construed as to excuse Acts
of Licenciousness, or justify Practices inconsis
=tant with the Peace or Safety of this State.

§ 39. And Whereas the ministers of the Gospel are
by their Profession dedicated to the Service of —
God & the Cure of Souls, & ought not to be diverted
from the Great Duties of their Function; therefore
no minister of the Gospel or Priest of any
denomination whatsoever shall at any time
hereafter under any Pretence or Discription —
whatever, be eligible to, or capable of holding any
civil or military Office or place within this —
State. —

§ 40 And whereas it is of the utmost Important
to the Safety of every State that it should
always be in a Condition of Defence and it is
the

[Handwritten document, right:]

80. That all wills in writing attested by
witnesses: shall be of the same force
or other conveyances; being registred
torys: office within forty dayes after
Death

That a widdow after the death of
have her Dower, And shall and
chife house of her husband forty
death of her husband, within which
dower shall be assigned unto her
shall be assigned unto her, the third
lands of her husband during
were endowed of less before
all lands and Heritages within
endences, shall be free from all
alienacons and from all
rys. Primier Seizins, year, day,
forfietures. upon the death of pa
all, vnnaturall, casuall or Judicia
Cases of High Treason only
That no person or persons which pro
Jesus Christ, shall at any time be
Molested, punished, disquieted or ca
for any difference in Opinion or
ligious concernment who do not
the civill peace of the Province

New York's famous CHARTER OF
LIBERTIES AND PRIVILEGES, October
17, 1683 (shown at right) proclaimed in
majestic sentences the right of religious
liberty. The charter so well expressed the
principle of freedom that it was restated,
almost word-for-word, when New York's
first CONSTITUTION was drafted in
1777. Section 38 of the '77 Constitution is
shown above.

These words which grant " . . . *free
exercise and enjoyment of religious profession . . . to all mankind . . .*" have stood
the test of time. They are repeated again
in Article I, section 3 of New York's revised Constitution of 1938.

And every Such person or persons may from time
to time and at all times freely have and fully Enjoy
his or their judgments or Consciences in matters of Religion, throughout all the province, they behaveing
themselves, peacably and quietly, and not Useing this
Liberty to Lycenciousnesse, nor to the Civill injury or
outward disturbance of others. Provided always, that
this Liberty or any thing contained herein to the contrary, shall never bee construed or improved to make
void the Settlement of any publique Minister on
Long=Island, whether such Settlement bee by two=
thirds of the voiass in any Towne thereon which
Shall alwayes include the Minor part or by Subscriptions of perticular Inhabitants in Said Townes,
Provided they are the two thirds thereof, Butt that
all Such Agreements, covenants and Subscriptions that
are there already made and had, that hereafter
Shall bee in this manner, consented to agreed and
subscribed, shall at all time and times hereafter bee
firm and Stable, and in confirmacon hereof it is
enacted by the Governor Councell and Representatives,
that all Such Summs of money So agreed on, consented to or Subscribed as aforesaid for maintenance
of Said publique Ministers, by the two thirds of
any Towne on Long=Island, Shall alwayes inclu-
=de the Minor part who shall bee regulated thereby
And.

Freedom of

Section 10. No law shall be passed abridging the right of the people peaceably to assemble and to petition the Government... thereof, nor shall any divorce be granted, otherwise than by due judicial proceedings; nor shall any lottery hereafter be authorized, ... sale of lottery tickets allowed, within this State.

Section 11. The people of this State, in their right of sovereignty, are deemed to possess the original and ultimate property ... to all lands within the jurisdiction of the State: and all lands the title to which shall fail, from a defect of heirs, shall revert, or escheat ... people.

Section 12. All feudal tenures of every description, with all their incidents are declared to be abolished, saving however all ... d services certain which at any time heretofore have been lawfully created or reserved.

Section 13. All lands within this State, are declared to be allodial, so that, subject only to the liability to escheat, the entire ... whole property is vested in the owners, according to the nature of their respective estates.

Section 14. No lease or grant of agricultural land, for a longer period than twelve years, hereafter made, in which shall ... d any rent or service of any kind, shall be valid.

Section 15. All fines, quarter sales, or other like restraints upon alienation ... void.

Section 16. No purcha... and seventy five; or which may ...

Section 17. ... said Colony, on the ninet... the convention of the State of New ... been repealed or altered; and su... ... alterations as the Legislature that ... ... repugnant to this Constitution, are ... ...ioners, whose duty it shall be to re... ... to the said Commissioners shall be... ... and expedient. And the said Commissioners shall specify such alterations and amend... ... as they shall deem proper, and they shall at all times make reports of their proceedings to the Legislature, when called upon to do so; ... Legislature shall pass laws regulating the tenure of office, the filling of vacancies therein; and the compensation of the said commissioners ... ll also provide for the publication of the said code, prior to its being presented to the Legislature for adoption.

with the expenses of the proceeding shall be paid by the person to be ben... Section 8. Every citizen may freely speak, abuse of that right; and no law shall be passed to restrain or abrid... indictments for libels, the truth may be given in evidence to the jury; and published with good motives, and for justifiable ends, the party sh... the fact

Section 18. All grants of land within this State, made by the King of Great Britain, or persons acting under his authority, after ... enth day of October, One thousand seven hundred and seventy five, shall be null and void; but nothing contained in this Constitution shall ... grants of land within this State, made by the authority of the said King or his predecessors, or shall annul any charters to bodies politic and corporate ... them made, before that day; or shall affect any such grants or charters since made by this State, or by persons acting under its authority ... impair the obligation of any debts contracted by the State, or individuals, or bodies corporate, or any other rights of property, or any suits, actions ... action, or other proceedings in Courts of justice.

Article II.

Section 1. Every male citizen of the age of twenty one years who shall have been a citizen for ten days, and an inhab... his State one year next preceding any election and for the last four months a resident of the county where he may offer his vote, ... entitled to vote at such election, in the election district of which he shall at the time be a resident, and not elsewhere, for all officers that ... or hereafter may be elective by the people; but such citizen shall have been for thirty days next preceding the election a resident of the ... from which the officer is to be chosen, for whom he offers his vote. But no man of color, unless he shall have been for three year...

Speech and Press...

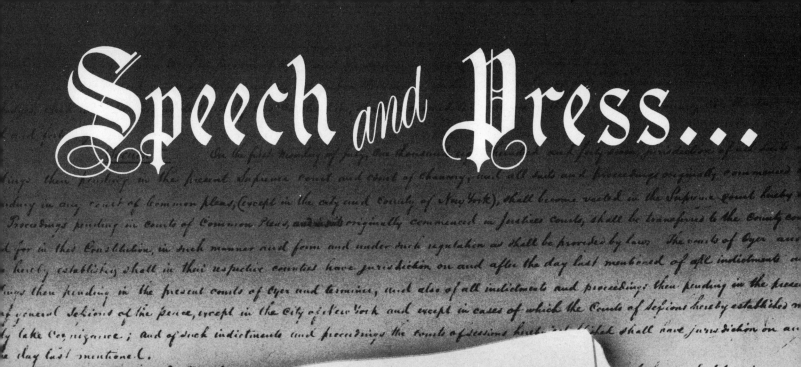

and publish his sentiments on all subjects, being responsible for the liberty of speech or of the press... In all criminal prosecutions or shall appear to the jury, that the matter charged as libellous is true, and was be acquitted; and the jury shall have the right to determine the law and

Article I, section 8, NEW YORK STATE CONSTITUTION, 1846.

Freedom of Speech and Press...

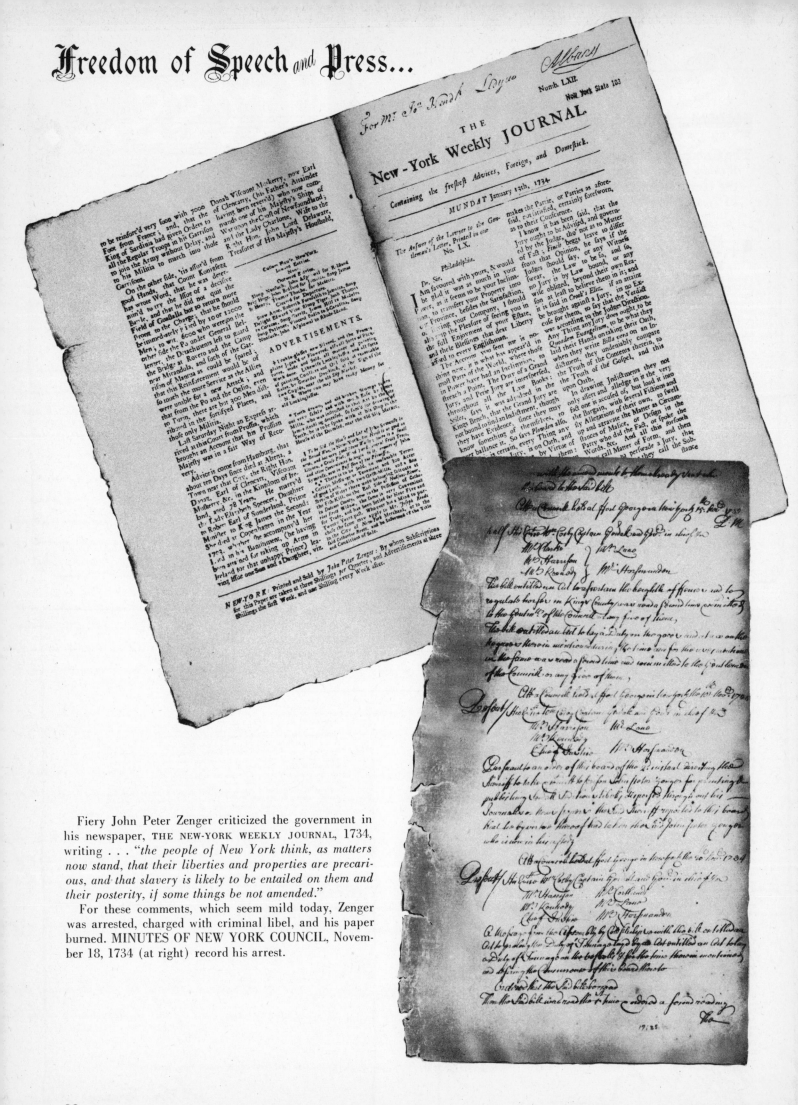

Fiery John Peter Zenger criticized the government in his newspaper, THE NEW-YORK WEEKLY JOURNAL, 1734, writing . . . *"the people of New York think, as matters now stand, that their liberties and properties are precarious, and that slavery is likely to be entailed on them and their posterity, if some things be not amended."*

For these comments, which seem mild today, Zenger was arrested, charged with criminal libel, and his paper burned. MINUTES OF NEW YORK COUNCIL, November 18, 1734 (at right) record his arrest.

[1]

The Complaint of *James Alexander* and *William Smith* to the Committee of the General Assembly of the Colony of *New-York*, *&c*.

Mr. Chairman ;

¶ I. IT is with the utmost Regret, that we attend this Committee in the Quality of Complainants; but the Matter of it too nearly affects us and the Liberties of this Country, to be buried in Silence. Had our personal Interests been solely concerned, we might have rested in a patient Expectation of a personal Remedy in some other Way: But when the Liberties of a Country are at Stake, and the Civil Enjoyments of a People sap'd at the very Foundation of them, it behoves every Man that loves his Country *to cry out and give publick Warning of the Danger*. This Duty incumbent upon all, engages us in particular, to inform you, That in the Term of *April* last, we, in the Case of *John Peter Zenger*, then depending in the Supream Court, filed Exceptions to the Commissions of the Justices there: The Tenour whereof follows.

The Attorney General, against *John Peter Zenger*. } Upon an Information for a Misdemeanour.

Exceptions humbly offered by *John Peter Zenger*, to the Power of the Honourable *James De Lancey*, Esq; to judge in this Cause.

The Defendant comes and prays Hearing of the Commission, by Virtue of which the Honourable *James De Lancey*, Esq; claims the Power and Authority to judge in this Cause, and it is read unto him in these Words;

'GEORGE *the second, by the Grace of God, of* Great Britain, France & Ireland, *King, Defender of the Faith, &c. To Our trusty & welbeloved* James De Lancey, *Esq; Greeting We reposing especial Trust & Confidence in your Integrity, Ability & Learning, have assigned, constituted and appointed, and We do by these Presents assign, constitute and appoint you the said* James De Lancey, *to be Chief Justice in and over our Province of* New-York, *in* America, *in the Room of* Lewis Moris, *Esq; Giving and by these Presents granting unto you, full Power and lawful Authority, to hear, try and determine all Pleas whatsoever, civil, criminal and mixt, according to the Laws, Statutes and Customs of Our Kingdom of* England, *and the Laws and Usages of Our said Province of* New-York, *not being repugnant thereto, and Execution of all Judgments of the said Court to award, and to make such Rules and Orders in the said Court, as may be found convenient and useful, and as near as may be agreeable to the Rules and Orders of Our Courts of King's Bench, Common Pleas, and Exchequer in* England. *To have hold and enjoy the said Office or Place of Chief Justice in and over Our said Province, with all and singular the Rights, Priviledges Profits Advantages, Salaries, Fees and Perquisites unto the said Place belonging, or in any Ways appertaining, in as full and ample Manner as any Person heretofore Chief Justice of Our said Province hath held and enjoyed, or of Right ought to have held and enjoyed the same, To you the said* James De Lancey, *for and* DURING OUR WILL AND PLEASURE. *In Testimony whereof We have caused these Our Letters to be made Patent, and the great Seal of Our said Province of* New-York *to be hereunto affixed. Witness Our trusty and welbeloved* William Cosby, *Esq; Our Captain General and Governour in Chief of Our Provinces of* New-York, New-Jersey, *and Terri-*
'*tories thereon depe*
'*the same, & Colone*
'in New-York, *th*
'*seventh Year of Ou*

Which being re
Zenger, by Protest

[3]

thority cannot be granted to, and excercised by, any one of the Justices of the *King's Bench*.

3*d*. For that the Form of the said Commission, is not founded on, nor warranted by, the Common Law, nor any Statute of *England*, nor of *Great Britain*, nor any Act of Assembly of this Colony.

4*th*. For that it appears by the Commission aforesaid, that the same is granted under the Seal of this Colony, by His Excellency *William Cosby*, Esq; Governour thereof, and it appears not, that the same was granted, neither was the same granted, by and with the Advice and Consent of His Majesty's Council of this Colony; without which Advice and Consent, His said Excellency could not grant the same.

Wherefore, and for many other Defects in the said Commission, this Defendant humbly hopes, that the Honourable *Frederick Philipse*, Esq; will not take Cognizance of this Cause, by Virtue of the Commission aforesaid.

James Alexander
William Smith.

¶ 2. Upon filing these Exceptions, we expected to be heard, as it was our undoubted Right by Law to be. And in Justification of our Conduct, we offered to prove, *That the Subject by Law has a Right to take such Exceptions, if he thinks the Commissions illegal*. We also offered to prove, *That the Exceptions taken were warranted by Law, and Valid*. But the Judges were pleased to say, *That they would neither hear us, nor allow the Exceptions*: But (as we conceive) *most arbitrarily and illegally* caused to be entred in the Minutes of the Court, the following Order.

'*At a Supream Court of Judicature, held for the Province of* New-York, *at the City-Hall of the City of* New-York, *on* Wednesday *the sixteenth Day of April*, 1735.

PRESENT, { The Honourable *James De Lancey*, Esq; Chief Justice. The Honourable *Frederick Philipse*, Esq; Second Justice.

'James Alexander *Esq; &* William Smith, *Attornies of this Court, having presumed* (NOTWITHSTANDING THEY WERE FORWARNED BY THE COURT OF THEIR DISPLEASURE, IF THEY SHOULD DO IT) *to sign, and having actually signed & put into Court, Exceptions, in the Name of* John Peter Zenger, *thereby denying the Legality of the Judges their Commissions, tho' in the usual Form*, AND THE BEING OF THIS SUPREAM COURT. *It is therefore ORDERED, That for the said CONTEMPT, the said* James Alexander *and* William Smith *be excluded from any further Practice in this Court, and that their Names be struck out of the Roll of Attornies of this Court*.

per Cur. *James Lyne*, Cl.

Mr. Chairman;

¶ 3. This Order is the Ground of Our Complaint. There are sundry Things in it which we shall take Notice of, in order to entitle our selves to the Relief of this Honourable House: The publick Interest of this Colony is greatly concerned in the Consequences of this Order; and for our own Parts, we think it exceeding hard to be deprived of our Subsistance, meerly for having done our Duty.

¶ 4. 'Tis a surprizing Thing to us, that the Gentlemen who made this Order, could proceed the Length they have done. The good Opinion we were willing to entertain of them disposed us to think, That they would never have done their Country and us so great an Injury. Could any Man have thought, that they would have *denyed the Subject a Liberty to take an Exception to their Commissions, when his Right to do so, is so clearly founded in Reason and Law?* He must be but little acquainted with the Laws of *England*, who could possibly make a Doubt, *Whether the Subject had such a Right?* But these Gentlemen, without Question, had seen that Matter fully treated of in the Case of Mr. *Van Dam*, in his Plea to the Jurisdiction of the Justices of the Supream Court,
he Argument on that Head had been de-
Manuscript, before the Day appointed for
printed before they made the abovesaid
14, to 33, *the Right of the Subject to take*
such

[7]

others: The Case was thus; King *James* the 2d co
of *Cambridge* to admit *a Papist* to the Degree of *Ma*
refused to do; and for that Contempt were cited befor
They appeared by their Vice Chancellor, and eight c
upon the Vice Chancellor *prayed, and had Time to answ*
Answer in Writing, and with Council, and by what Co
Time appointed they pleaded to the Jurisdiction of the Court, both as to that particular Case they were cited for, and as to the whole Power of the Court, by setting forth the Act of 16*th* of *Charles* the first, that enacted, that no such Court as that should be afterwards held. Which Plea was received, and read, and when read, the Chancellor *JEFFERYS* asked, if it was signed? Whereupon it was answered, *Yes My Lord*; and then the Matter was taken into Consideration for a Week: But it appears not by this Case, that even that wicked Man, the Chancellor *JEFFERYS*, ever so much as thought, that those Council acted amiss, for advising or signing of that, or the former Plea in the Bishop of *London*'s Case: Tho' in the last Case, to the shame of that Court, *JEFFERYS* pronounced the Judgment of it, which was, *That, as a Mark of His Majesty's and their Lordships* DISPLEASURE, *they thought fit to appoint, that the Vice Chancellor should be thenceforth deprived of that Office*. All which appears in the 4*th Vol.* of the *State Tryals*, from *pag*. 250. to 259.

¶ 14. These Authorities, with what is referred to in the Argument of Mr. *Van Dam*'s Council, are a full Proof, that it is by Law the Right of the Subject to take Exception, either to the Jurisdiction of the Court, or the Commission of a Judge. And if this be the Right of the Subject, how consistent is it with the GREAT CHARTER to deny it to him? It is said there, *Nulli negabimus, nulli differemus Justitiam vel Rectum. We will deny no Man, we will delay to no Man, Justice or Right*.

Now this Law was made our Birth-Right (see My Lord *Coke*'s Comment. upon 2*d Inst*. 56.) And to observe this Law, not only the King, at His Coronation, but all his Judges of Common Law, are or ought to be sworn. And if this is the Subjects Right, what Judge, without Violation of his Oath, can deny it? And how can it, consistent with either Reason, Law or common Sense, be termed *a CONTEMPT* to claim that Right? Or for Council to sign and file Exceptions in Consequence of that Right?

¶ 15. In the next Place we observe, that the Suggestion, in the said Order, *That the Exception denys the Being of the Supream Court*, is altogether without Truth and groundless. Had the Supream Court no other Foundation than the Judges Commissions, there might have been some Truth in that Suggestion. In such Case, to deny the Lawfulness of their Commissions, would be to deny the Being of the Court: But it is well known, that the Being of the Supream Court has a quite different Foundation.

¶ 16. It was, till lately, understood to have been founded on Ordinances, several of which have been made from Time to Time, either to give or continue its Being, the last of which was published in the Supream Court, in the Presence, and by Order, of these Gentlemen, and bears date no longer ago than the 19*th March*, in the sixth Year of His present Majesty's Reign. But suppose it to exist or have its being *by the Common Law*, as some have lately imagined, and which seems to be Mr. Chief Justice's Opinion (see his Charge to the Grand Jury of 15*th January*, 1733. *pag*. 4. *Gentlemen*, - - - - [whole Paragraph to] - - - - *now*.) Yet in either Case, it doth not derive its Being from the

[19]

New-York, *ss*.

IN Obedience to an Order of the Honourable the General Assembly, dated the 24th Day of October *last*, James Alexander *and* William Smith, *being duly sworn on the holy Evangelists, on their Oath do declare, That the preceeding Paper contains a true, full and compleat Copy of the Complaint which they offered to the Committee of Grievances, against the Judges of the Supream Court, and of all that they offered and said before the said Committee on the 23d Day of* October *last, at the House of Mr.* John D'honneur, *by Way of Complaint against the said Judges, to the Best of the Knowledge of these Deponents. EXCEPT that in the 22d Paragraph some Words are inserted between these Marks [ ] which were designed to have been said in that Place, but they believe they were by Mistake omitted to be spoken. And EXCEPT that the Words* Mr. Chairman *were oftner spoken than what appears by the preceeding Copy. And EXCEPT some Words spoken* extempore, *the Substance of which they believe is contained in the Marginal Note on the last Paragraph. And EXCEPT the Marginal Notes and Numbers of the Paragraphs, which have been since added. The Deponents DECLARING, that what they said* extempore, *before and after the Complaint, in excepting to Judge* Philipse's *being one of the Committee, and other Exceptions then made* extempore, *not having been reduced to Writing before they were offered, they do not esteem any Part of their said Complaint; neither is it in their Power to remember exactly what was said on that Occasion, nor do they conceive it was the Intention of the General Assembly, to order the Delivery of a Copy of that to the Judges. And farther the Deponents say not.*

Ja. Alexander.
Wm. Smith.

Sworn the Twenty seventh Day of *December*, 1735. Before

S. Johnson.

The people watched with excitement Zenger's trial. First, his lawyers were disbarred for questioning the validity of the judges to act in the case. Their COMPLAINT, dated December 27, 1735, argued that such action was contrary to Magna Carta.

Andrew Hamilton, who was the key lawyer for the defense, summed up his argument, saying that if what Zenger had printed in his newspaper was true, then he should not be found guilty. The law, Hamilton claimed, upheld . . . "*the liberty both of expression and opposing arbitrary power, in these parts of the world at least, by speaking and writing truth.*"

Pages from THE TRIAL OF JOHN PETER ZENGER (shown on the opposite page) lists the names of jurymen as they were called and sworn for this history-making trial. Then follows the King's indictment, which charged . . . *"that John Peter Zenger, late of the City of New York, Printer, . . . did falsly, seditiously and scandalously print and publish, and cause to be printed and published, a certain false, malicious, seditious, scandalous Libel, intituled, The New-York Weekly Journal."*

Andrew Hamilton (pictured above in the court-room) smashed the prosecution's case by proving that what Zenger had published was true, hence he could not be found guilty. The jury agreed with Hamilton, as the last page of the Trial Papers show.

Their verdict of . . .*"Not Guilty"* was greeted by . . . *"three Huzzas in the Hall, which crowded with People; and the next Day Zenger was discharged from his imprisonment."* Zenger was cheered by everyone for his magnificent stand, he had fought for the right of a free press and had won. He became the father of a free press in the United States.

THE
TRIAL
OF
John Peter Zenger,
OF

NEW-YORK, PRINTER;

Who was Tried and Acquitted,

For PRINTING and PUBLISHING a LIBEL against the Government,

WITH

The PLEADINGS and ARGUMENTS on both Sides.

Ita CUIQUE *eveniat, ut de* REPUBLICA *meruit.* CIC.

LONDON:

Printed for P. BROWN, in *Fleet-Street.* MDCCLII.

[Price One Shilling and Sixpence.]

Clerk. Yes, I believe it is.

Ch. J. How came the Names of the Jurors to be misplaced in the Pannel annexed to the *Venire*?

Sheriff. I have returned the Jurors in the same Order in which the Clerk gave them to me.

Ch. J. Let the Names of the Jurors be ranged in the Order they were struck, agreeable to the Copy here in Court.

Which was done accordingly. And the Jury, whose Names were as follows, were called and sworn.

Hermanus Rutgers,	*Egbert van Borsom,*
Stanly Holmes,	*Thomas Hunt,*
Edward Man,	*Benjamin Hildreth,* Forem.
John Bell,	*Abraham Keteltas,*
Samuel Weaver,	*John Goelet,*
Andries Marschalk,	*Hercules Wendover.*

Mr. Attorney-General opened the Information, which was as follows:

Mr. Attorney. May it please your Honours, and you Gentlemen of the Jury: The Information, now before the Court, and to which the Defendant Zenger has pleaded *Not Guilty,* is an Information for printing and publishing *a false, scandalous and seditious Libel,* in which his Excellency the Governor of this Province, who is the King's immediate Representative here, is greatly and unjustly scandalized, as a Person that has no Regard to Law nor Justice: With much more, as will appear upon reading the Information. This of Libelling is what has always been discouraged as a Thing that tends to create Differences among Men, ill Blood among the People, and oftentimes great Bloodshed between the Party libelling and the Party libelled. There can be no Doubt but you Gentlemen of the Jury will have the same ill Opinion of such Practices, as the Judges have always shewn upon such Occasions: But I shall say no more at this Time, un-

---

til you hear the Information, which is as follows:

"*New-York,* Supreme Court.
"Of the Term of *January,* in the Eighth Year of the Reign of our Sovereign Lord King GEORGE IId, &c.

"*New-York, ss.* BE it remembered, That *Richard Bradley,* Esq; Attorney-General of Our Sovereign Lord the King, for the Province of *New-York,* who for Our said Lord the King in this Part prosecutes, in his own proper Person comes here into the Court of Our said Lord the King, and for Our said Lord the King gives the Court here to understand, and be informed, — That *John Peter Zenger,* late of the City of *New-York,* Printer, (being a seditious Person, and a frequent Printer and Publisher of false News and seditious Libels, and wickedly and maliciously devising the Government of Our said Lord the King of this His Majesty's Province of *New-York,* under the Administration of His Excellency *William Cosby,* Esq; Captain-General and Governor in Chief of the said Province, to traduce, scandalize and vilify; and His Excellency the said Governor, and the Ministers and Officers of Our said Lord the King of and for the said Province to bring into Suspicion and the ill Opinion of the Subjects of Our said Lord the King residing within the said Province) the Twenty-eighth Day of *January,* in the Seventh Year of the Reign of Our Sovereign Lord *George* the Second, by the Grace of God of *Great-Britain, France* and *Ireland,* King, Defender of the Faith, &c. at the City of *New-York,* did falsly, seditiously and scandalously print and publish, and cause to be printed and published, a certain false, malicious, seditious, scandalous Libel, intituled, *The New-York Weekly Journal, containing the freshest Advices foreign and domestic*; in which Libel (of

---

been always looked upon as a Crime; and no Government can be safe without it be punished."

Now you are to consider, whether these Words I have read to you, do not tend to beget an ill Opinion of the Administration of the Government? To tell us, those who are employed know nothing of the Matter, and those who do know are not employed; Men are not adapted to Offices, but Offices to Men, out of a particular Regard to their Interest, and not to their Fitness for the Places; this is the Purport of these Papers.

Mr. Hamilton. I humbly beg your Honour's Pardon; I am very much misapprehended, if you suppose what I said was so designed.

Sir, you know, I made an Apology for the Freedom I found myself under a Necessity of, using upon this Occasion. I said, there was nothing personal designed; it arose from the Nature of our Defence.

The Jury withdrew, and in a small Time returned, and being asked by the Clerk, " Whether they were agreed of their Verdict, and whether *John Peter Zenger* was guilty of printing and publishing the Libels in the Information mentioned?" They answered by *Thomas Hunt,* their Foreman, NOT GUILTY.

Upon which there were three Huzzas in the Hall, which crowded with People; and the next Day Zenger was discharged from his Imprisonment.

A P-

Right to Vote...

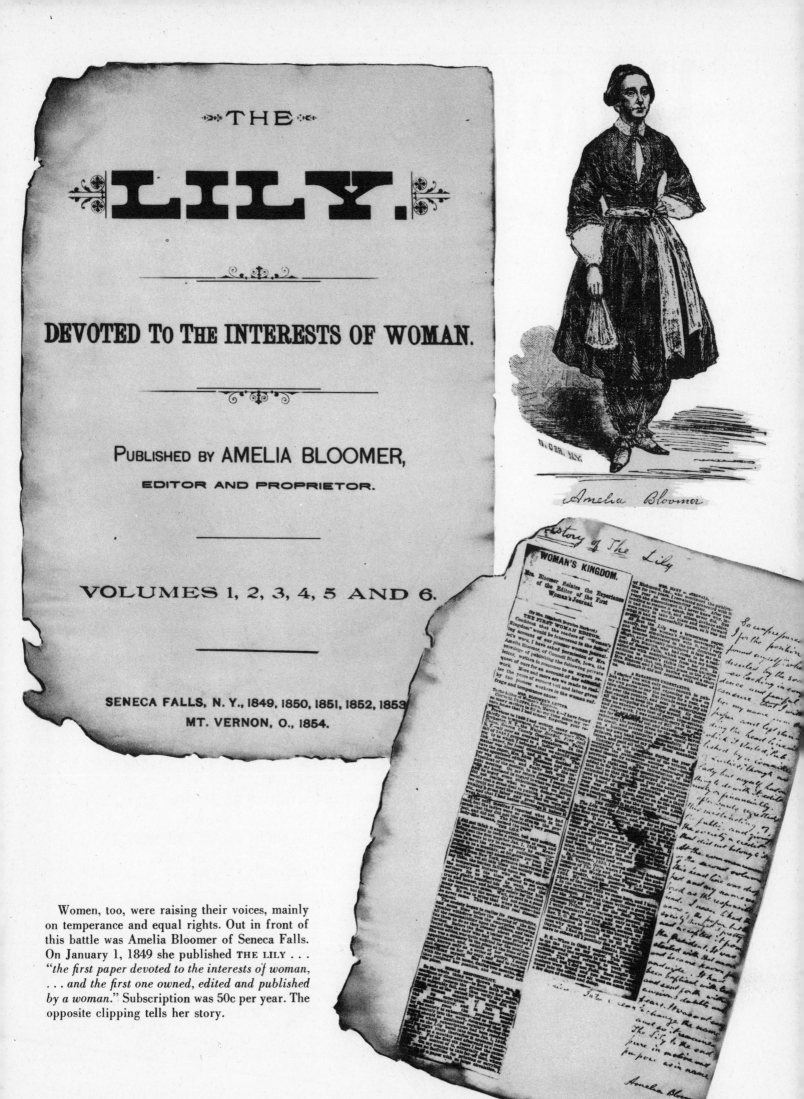

THE LILY.

DEVOTED TO THE INTERESTS OF WOMAN.

PUBLISHED BY AMELIA BLOOMER,

EDITOR AND PROPRIETOR.

VOLUMES 1, 2, 3, 4, 5 AND 6.

SENECA FALLS, N. Y., 1849, 1850, 1851, 1852, 1853
MT. VERNON, O., 1854.

Amelia Bloomer

Women, too, were raising their voices, mainly on temperance and equal rights. Out in front of this battle was Amelia Bloomer of Seneca Falls. On January 1, 1849 she published THE LILY . . . *"the first paper devoted to the interests of woman, . . . and the first one owned, edited and published by a woman."* Subscription was 50c per year. The opposite clipping tells her story.

Right to Vote...

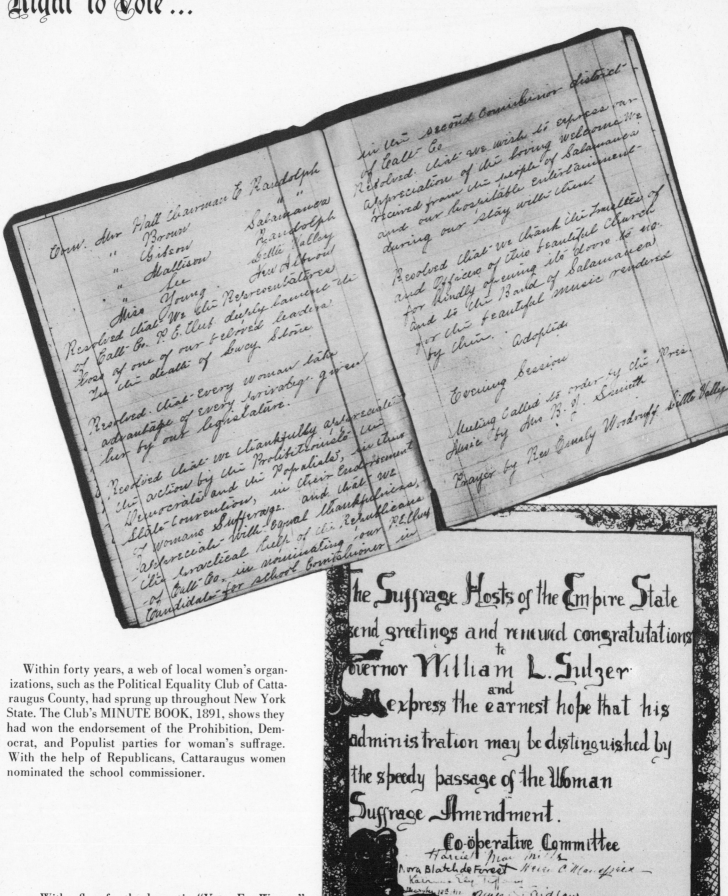

Within forty years, a web of local women's organizations, such as the Political Equality Club of Cattaraugus County, had sprung up throughout New York State. The Club's MINUTE BOOK, 1891, shows they had won the endorsement of the Prohibition, Democrat, and Populist parties for woman's suffrage. With the help of Republicans, Cattaraugus women nominated the school commissioner.

With a flare for the dramatic, "Votes For Women" pilgrims rallied in New York City, December 16, 1912 and marched on Albany to greet Governor-elect William Sulzer with a PETITION urging . . . *"The speedy passage of the Woman Suffrage Amendment."*

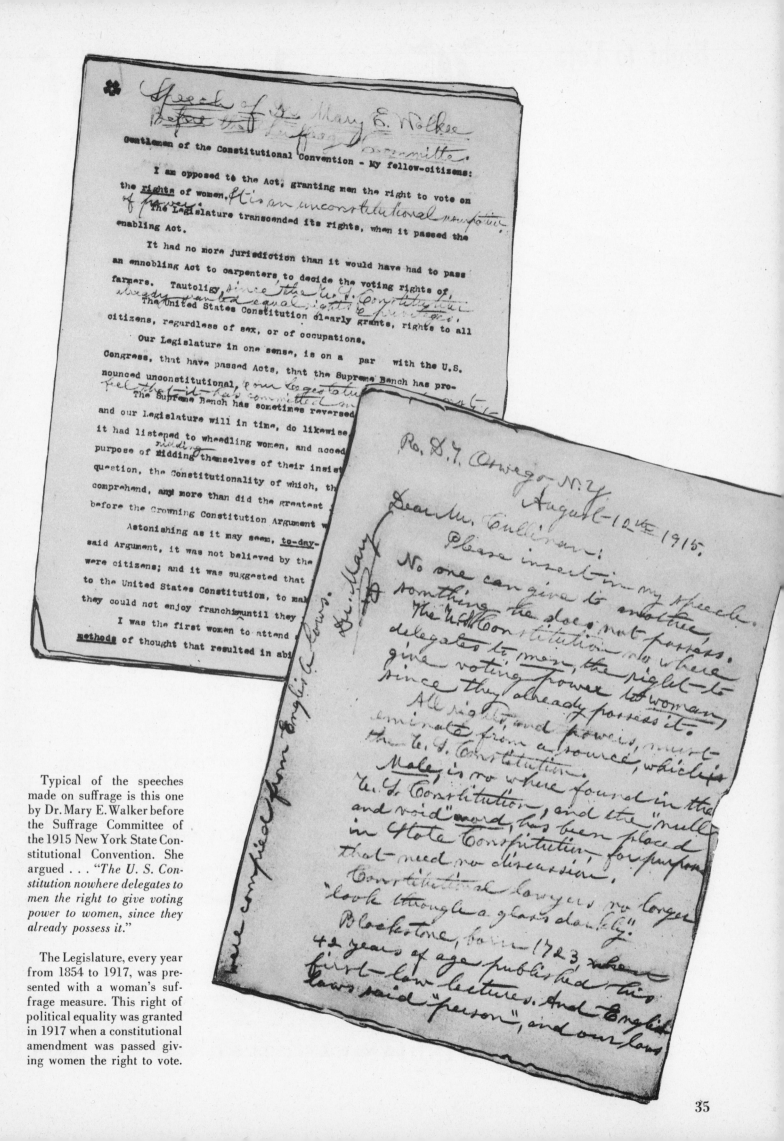

Typical of the speeches made on suffrage is this one by Dr. Mary E. Walker before the Suffrage Committee of the 1915 New York State Constitutional Convention. She argued . . . *"The U. S. Constitution nowhere delegates to men the right to give voting power to women, since they already possess it."*

The Legislature, every year from 1854 to 1917, was presented with a woman's suffrage measure. This right of political equality was granted in 1917 when a constitutional amendment was passed giving women the right to vote.

Freedom of

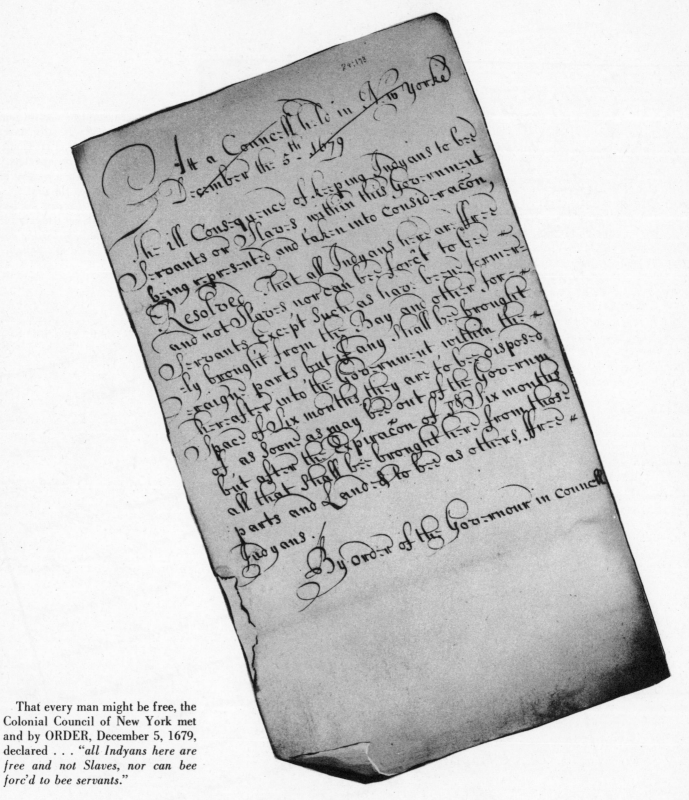

That every man might be free, the Colonial Council of New York met and by ORDER, December 5, 1679, declared . . . "*all Indyans here are free and not Slaves, nor can bee forc'd to bee servants.*"

THE INDIAN WAS FREED

Person...

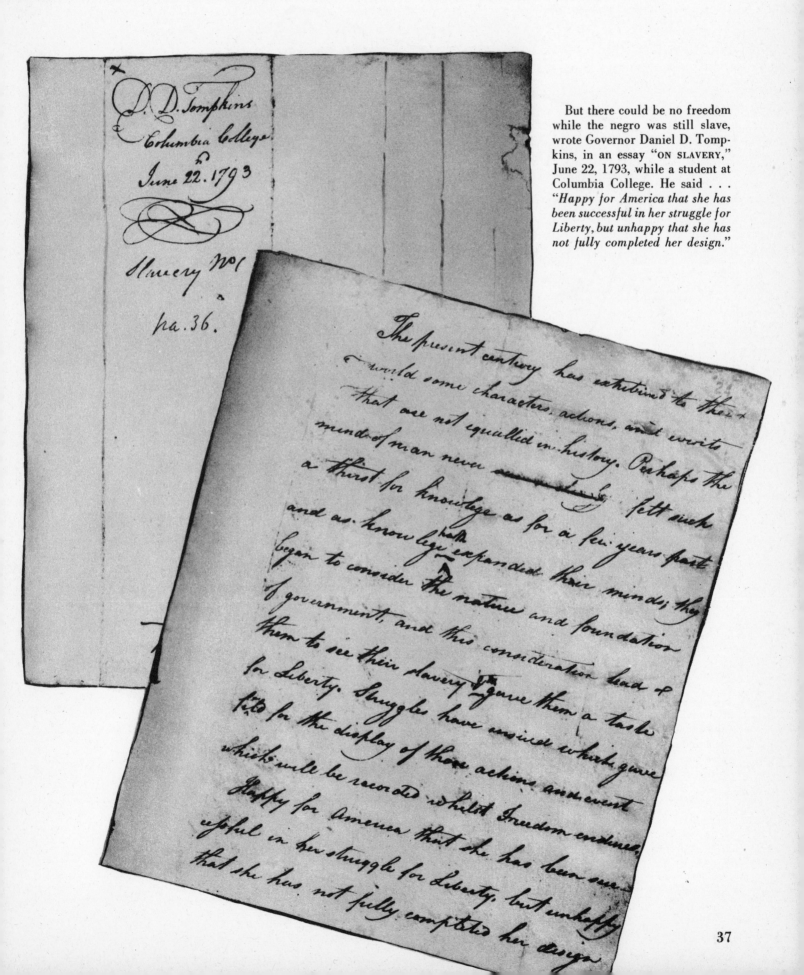

But there could be no freedom while the negro was still slave, wrote Governor Daniel D. Tompkins, in an essay "ON SLAVERY," June 22, 1793, while a student at Columbia College. He said . . . *"Happy for America that she has been successful in her struggle for Liberty, but unhappy that she has not fully completed her design."*

An Act for the gradual abolition of Slavery.

Be it enacted by the people of the State of New York represented in Senate and Assembly, That any child born of a slave within this State after the fourth day of July next, shall be deemed and adjudged to be born free: Provided nevertheless that such child shall be the servant of the legal proprietor of his or her mother, until such servant if a male shall arrive at the age of twenty eight years, and if a female at the age of twenty five years.

And be it further enacted, That such proprietor his, heir, or their Heirs or Assigns shall be entitled to the service of such Child until he or she shall arrive to the age aforesaid, in the same manner as if such child had been bound to service by the Overseers of the Poor.

And be it further enacted, That every person being an Inhabitant of this State who shall be entitled to the service of a child born after the fourth day of July as aforesaid, shall within nine months after the birth of such child, cause to be delivered to the Clerk of the City or Town, whereof such person shall be an Inhabitant, a certificate in writing containing the name and addition of such master or mistress, and the name age, and sex of every child so born, which certificate shall be, by the said Clerk recorded in a Book to be by him for that purpose provided, which record shall be good and sufficient evidence of the age of such child, And the Clerk of such City or Town shall receive from said person twelve cents for every child so registered, and if any such person neglects to make a return of every such child as aforesaid to said Clerk within nine months after the Birth thereof, such person shall forfeit and pay Five Dollars for every such offence, to be sued for and recovered by the Clerk of the City or Town in which such person resides,

till it arrives at the age of one year, And every owner omitting
to give notice in due form as aforesaid shall be answerable
for the maintainance of every such child, until the arrival
of the respective periods of servitude specified in the first sec
=tion of this Act

And be it further enacted that it shall be lawful for the
owner of any slave immediately after the passing of this Act
to manumit such slave, by a certificate for that purpose
under his hand and seal.

State of New York
    In Senate March 28th 1799.
This Bill having been read the third time
Resolved that the Bill do pass.
    By Order of the Senate.

Stephen Van Rensselaer
President

State of New York
    In Assembly February 9th 1799.
This Bill having been read the third time
Resolved that the Bill do pass
    By order of the Assembly

Dirck Ten Broeck Speaker

On March 29, 1799, the Senate and Assembly, expressing the will of the people, passed AN ACT FOR THE GRADUAL ABOLITION OF SLAVERY, saying . . . "*that every child born of a slave within this State after the fourth of July next, shall be deemed and adjudged to be born free. . . .*"

The law called for all masters to register the names of children born after this date. A fee of 12 cents was charged; and if the master failed, he was fined $5.00.

Freedom of Person...

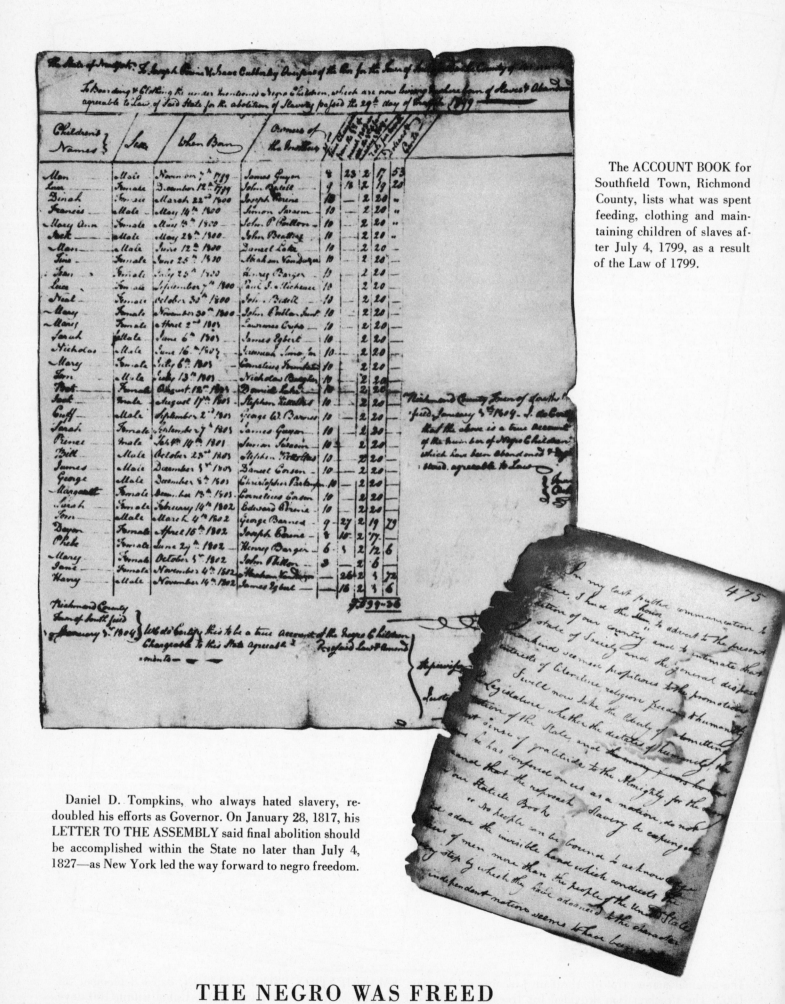

The ACCOUNT BOOK for Southfield Town, Richmond County, lists what was spent feeding, clothing and maintaining children of slaves after July 4, 1799, as a result of the Law of 1799.

Daniel D. Tompkins, who always hated slavery, redoubled his efforts as Governor. On January 28, 1817, his LETTER TO THE ASSEMBLY said final abolition should be accomplished within the State no later than July 4, 1827—as New York led the way forward to negro freedom.

THE NEGRO WAS FREED

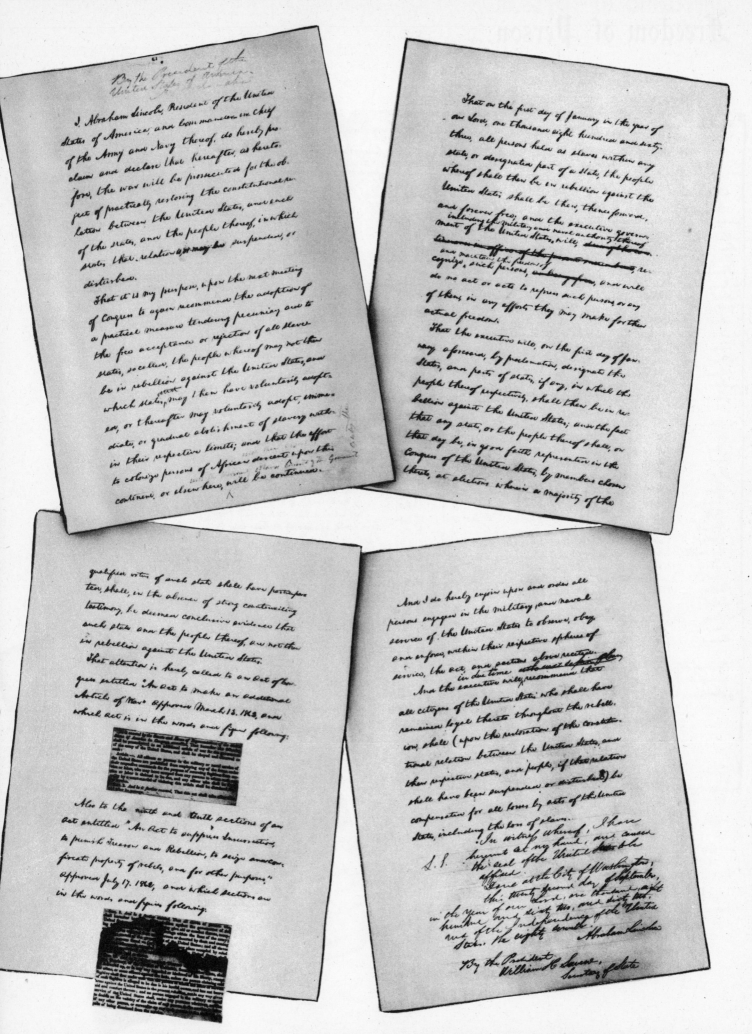

The original manuscript of Abraham Lincoln's preliminary EMANCIPATION PROCLAMATION, dated September 22, 1862. The Proclamation provided for freedom of slaves if seceding states did not return to the Union within 100 days.

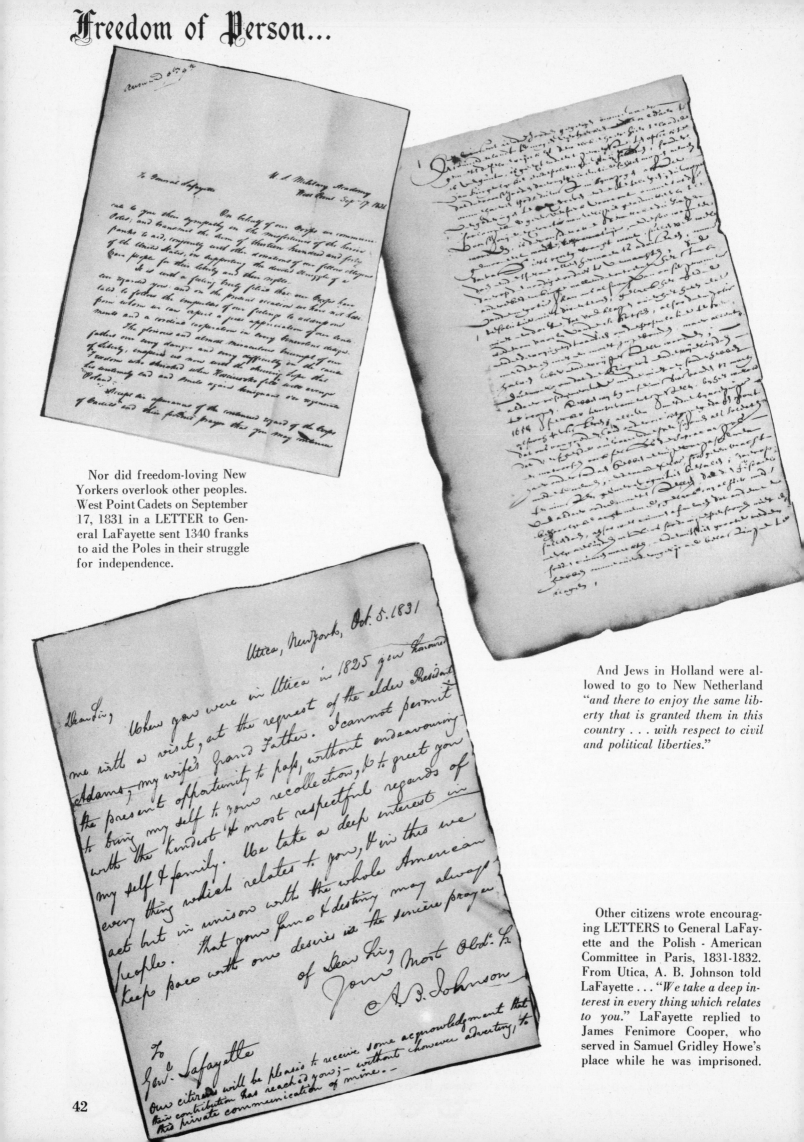

Nor did freedom-loving New Yorkers overlook other peoples. West Point Cadets on September 17, 1831 in a LETTER to General LaFayette sent 1340 franks to aid the Poles in their struggle for independence.

And Jews in Holland were allowed to go to New Netherland *"and there to enjoy the same liberty that is granted them in this country . . . with respect to civil and political liberties."*

Other citizens wrote encouraging LETTERS to General LaFayette and the Polish-American Committee in Paris, 1831-1832. From Utica, A. B. Johnson told LaFayette . . . *"We take a deep interest in every thing which relates to you."* LaFayette replied to James Fenimore Cooper, who served in Samuel Gridley Howe's place while he was imprisoned.

To create "*a bond of union . . . a source of prosperity for its inhabitants . . .*" the New York City Common Council MEMORIALIZES the Legislature, February 20, 1816, to complete navigation to the ocean through the Hudson River from the Great Lakes by considering "*the great important Canal question.*"

In the same spirit the Legislature granted a CHARTER to the State's first railroad, The Mohawk and Hudson, April 17, 1826, connecting Albany with Schenectady. This was the first link in the present vast New York Central System.

The first locomotive and train of passenger-cars ever run in the State of New York.

Freedom of

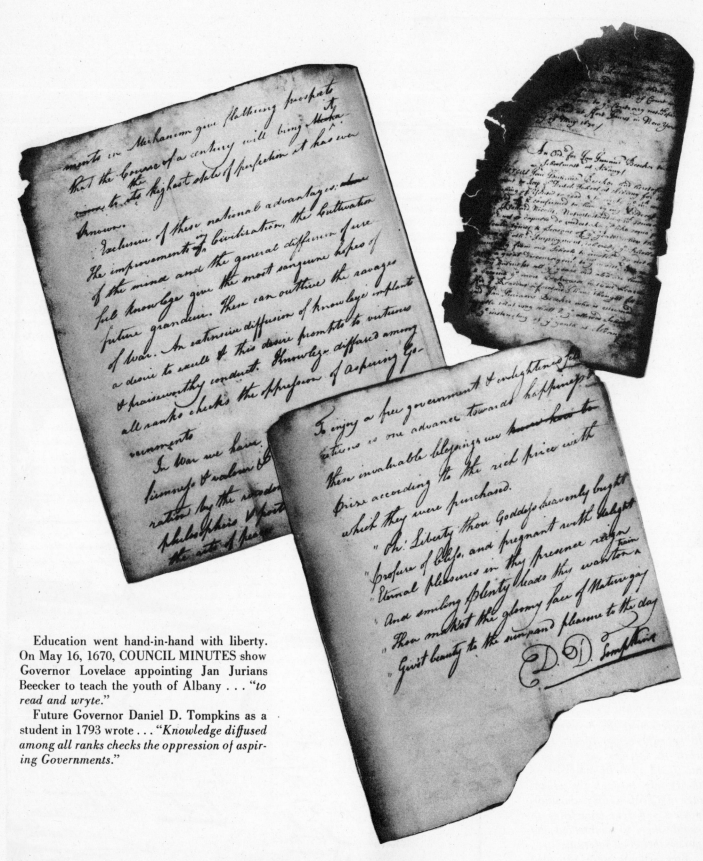

Education went hand-in-hand with liberty. On May 16, 1670, COUNCIL MINUTES show Governor Lovelace appointing Jan Jurians Beecker to teach the youth of Albany . . . *"to read and wryte."*

Future Governor Daniel D. Tompkins as a student in 1793 wrote . . . *"Knowledge diffused among all ranks checks the oppression of aspiring Governments."*

THE NEED FOR SCHOOLS

Education...

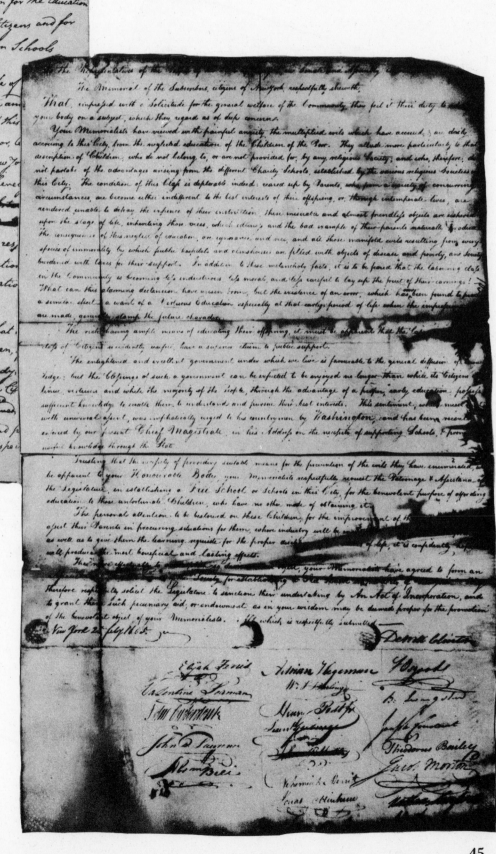

Every child must be educated, stressed **DeWitt Clinton** — the father of free public schools, February 25, 1805. He described how poor children . . . *"miserable and almost friendless objects are ushered upon the stage of life, inheriting those vices, which idleness, and the bad example of their parents naturally produce...."* He warned that... *"a government can be expected to be enjoyed no longer than while its Citizens continue virtuous and while the majority of the People, through the advantage of a proper, early education possess sufficient knowledge to enable them to understand and pursue their best interests."*

Free schools were provided for the poor by ACT of Legislature, 1804.

Freedom of Education...

The New York Legislature chartered Cornell University by ACT, April 27, 1865. Chief aim ... "to teach such branches of learning as are related to agriculture and the mechanic arts, including military tactics, in order to promote the liberal and practical education of the industrial classes ...."

Immigrants coming to America found New York school doors open to them. The Legislature supported with State funds New York City's ECONOMICAL SCHOOL, founded in 1819, so French children might learn to speak English.

And Thomas Jefferson, in a letter from Monticello, October 6, 1823, asked for a copy of Columbia College's Code of Regulations so he might set up the University of Virginia.

EDUCATIONAL OPPORTUNITY FOR ALL

Freedom of Education...

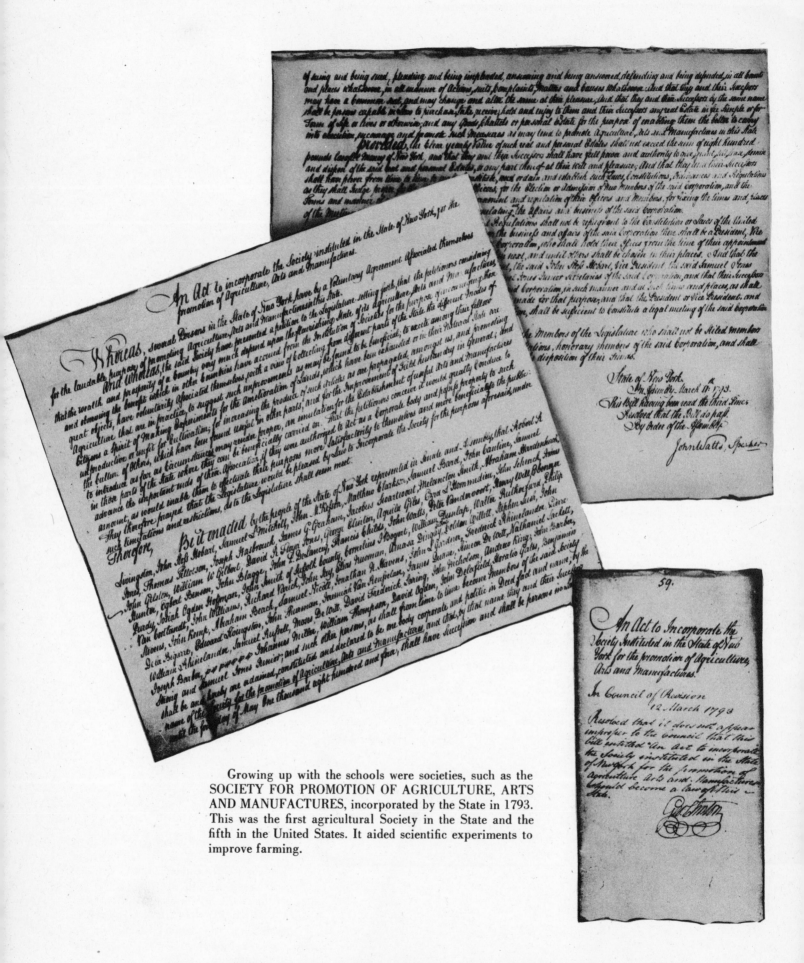

Growing up with the schools were societies, such as the SOCIETY FOR PROMOTION OF AGRICULTURE, ARTS AND MANUFACTURES, incorporated by the State in 1793. This was the first agricultural Society in the State and the fifth in the United States. It aided scientific experiments to improve farming.

TO ADVANCE SCIENCE, MANUFACTURING

13

Annually to report to the Legislature the State of Literature in Columbia College, and the several Academies incorporated within this State: being enjoined by Law, We the Regents of the University beg Leave, in the Discharge of this Duty, to call the Attention of the Senate and Assembly to an Object, which has, with ... our Wisdom, been selected, ... entitled ... particular Manner to the care ... Support of the Public. —

Upon a former Occasion we ... Liberty to mention that we had ... most pleasing Prospect of the Progress and Advancement of Science; and it ... now affords us great Satisfaction to ... that our Expectations upon this Subject ... have in some Degree been realis... The Number of Students in the Colle... not less than during the preced... Year; and in the two Academies ... porated by us, it has conside... increased. — Erasmus Hall gi... tion to sixty, and Clinton A... about ninety Pupils. — These ... Seminaries have been vis... ...rent Members of our Corp... we find that the Plan of Educat... pursued in them has not varied ma... rially since our last Report. — In all of them, the Abilities and Exertions of the Teachers, as well as the Diligence and

Washington Oct. 14th 182...

Dear Sir

I offer my acknowledg... ments for the interest you have taken in promoting the School over which you preside. I have enclosed a draft hastily drawn up of my plan for the government of the School which I beg you to submit to ... it the Gentlemen associated with you for consideration & amendment. If after my ... that the School will proceed and the advantages I anticipated will be realized

with respect Yours sincerely S. Van Rensselaer

Sam. Blatchford, Pres.

Regents of the University of the State of New York, in a REPORT to the Legislature, December 7, 1788, expressed satisfaction with the development of scientific studies at Columbia College.

CORRESPONDENCE of Stephan Van Rensselaer and Samuel Blatchford discuss the founding of Rensselaer Polytechnic Institute, 1825.

Freedom of Education...

At Troy, New York, 1825, Stephan Van Rensselaer opened the first scientific school in the United States. His LETTER to Blatchford, the school's first president, contained RPI's Constitution, stating its purpose ... *"to instruct persons ... in the Application of Science To The Common Purposes of Life."* The Catalogue of 1845 lists some of the courses offered.

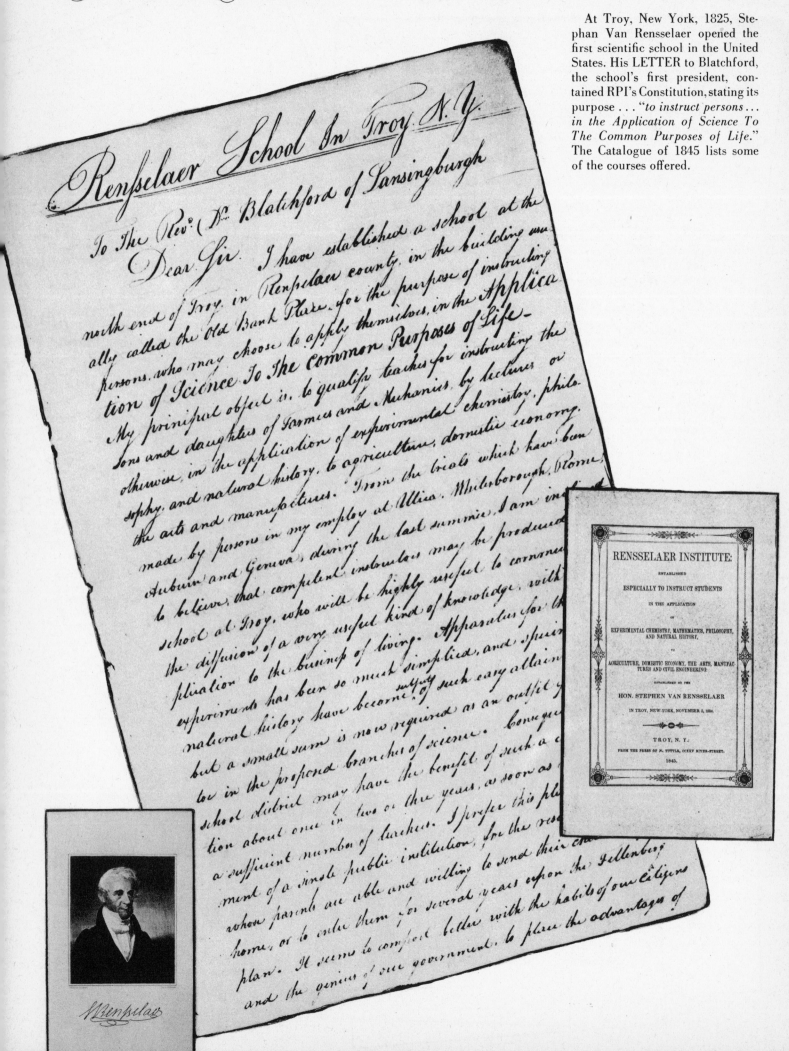

Senate, No. 2876

CHAP 753

AN ACT

To amend the education law, in relation to complaints against educational institutions for alleged discrimination in the admission of applicants

The People of the State of New York, represented in Senate and Assembly, do enact as follows:

Section 1. Chapter twenty-one of the laws of nineteen hundred nine, entitled "An act relating to education, constituting chapter sixteen of the consolidated laws," as amended and recodified by chapter eight hundred twenty of the laws of nineteen hundred forty-seven, is hereby amended by adding thereto a new section, to be section three hundred thirteen, to read as follows:

§ 313. (1) Declaration of policy. It is hereby declared to be the policy of the state that the American ideal of equality of opportunity requires that students, otherwise qualified, be admitted to educational institutions without regard to race, color, religion,

---

2

creed or national origin. except that, with regard to religious or denominational educational institutions, students, otherwise qualified, shall have the equal opportunity to attend therein without discrimination because of race, color or national origin. It is a fundamental American right for members of various religious faiths to establish and maintain educational institutions exclusively or primarily for students of their own religious faith or to effectuate the religious principles in furtherance of which they are maintained. Nothing herein contained shall impair or abridge that right.

(2) Definitions. (a) Educational institution means any educational institution of post-secondary grade subject to the visitation, examination or inspection by the state board of regents or the state commissioner of education.

(b) A religious or denominational educational institution means an educational institution which is operated, supervised or controlled by a religious or denominational organization and which holds to the state commissioner of education that it is a religious or denominational educational institution.

(3) Unfair educational practices. It shall be an unfair educational practice for an educational institution after September first, nineteen hundred forty-eight:

(a) To exclude or limit or otherwise discriminate against any person or persons seeking admission as students to such institution because of race, religion, creed, color, or national origin; except that nothing in this section shall be deemed to affect, in any way, the right of a religious or denominational educational institution to

---

7

(8) The commissioner shall include in his annual report to the legislature (1) a resume of the nature and substance of the cases disposed of through public hearings, and (2) recommendations for further action to eliminate discrimination in education if such is needed.

§ 2. This act shall take effect July first, nineteen hundred forty-eight.

Approved
Thomas E. Dewey

APR 3 1948

Freedom of

Man's right to work was protected in New York as early as 1665 when the DUKE'S LAWS, passed in Convention to "*admonish Masters and Dames of whom servants complained of tyrranical and cruel abuse.*"

Lansingburgh and Troy carpenters organized one of the first unions, June 19, 1790, adopting RULES AND REGULATIONS "*for the good government of themselves, and the benefit of their employers.*"

PROTECTION FROM ABUSE

Barrel-makers of South and East Hampton PETITION the Government, October 13, 1675, against unfair competition from Boston coopers who come in for the winter season.

Labor...

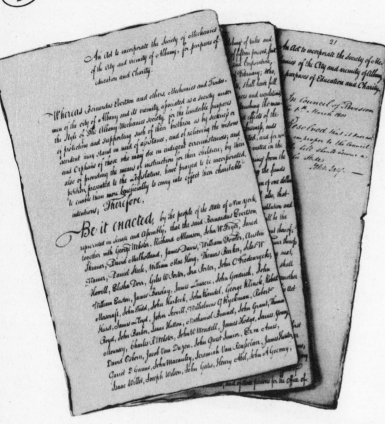

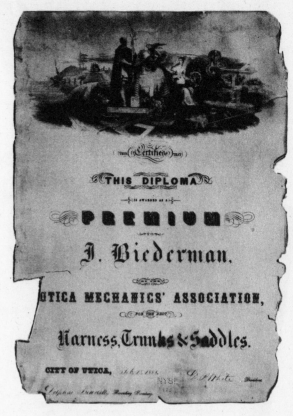

Utica's Mechanics' Association rewarded "good work" with this DIPLOMA.

In Albany, the Mechanics' Society organized March 6, 1801 *"to protect their brethren who needed help while sick or injured, and to aid widows and educate orphans of workers."* The Society's REGISTER lists Philip Hooker, noted architect, as a carpenter; Jeremiah Van Rensselaer, as a painter.

Martin I. Townsend, in a SPEECH, told the Mechanics and Labourers Association of Troy and Albia, 1835, of labor's dignity, its opportunity for self-advancement.

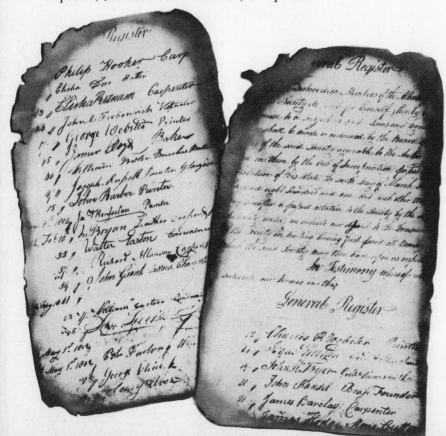

Freedom of Labor...

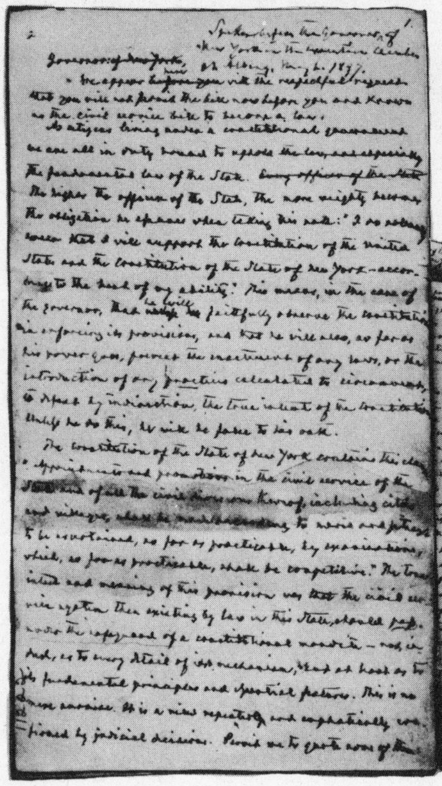

Carl Schurz, in an ADDRESS urged Governor Frank Black to veto the Civil Service bill of 1897, because it drew distinction between . . . "merit and fitness."

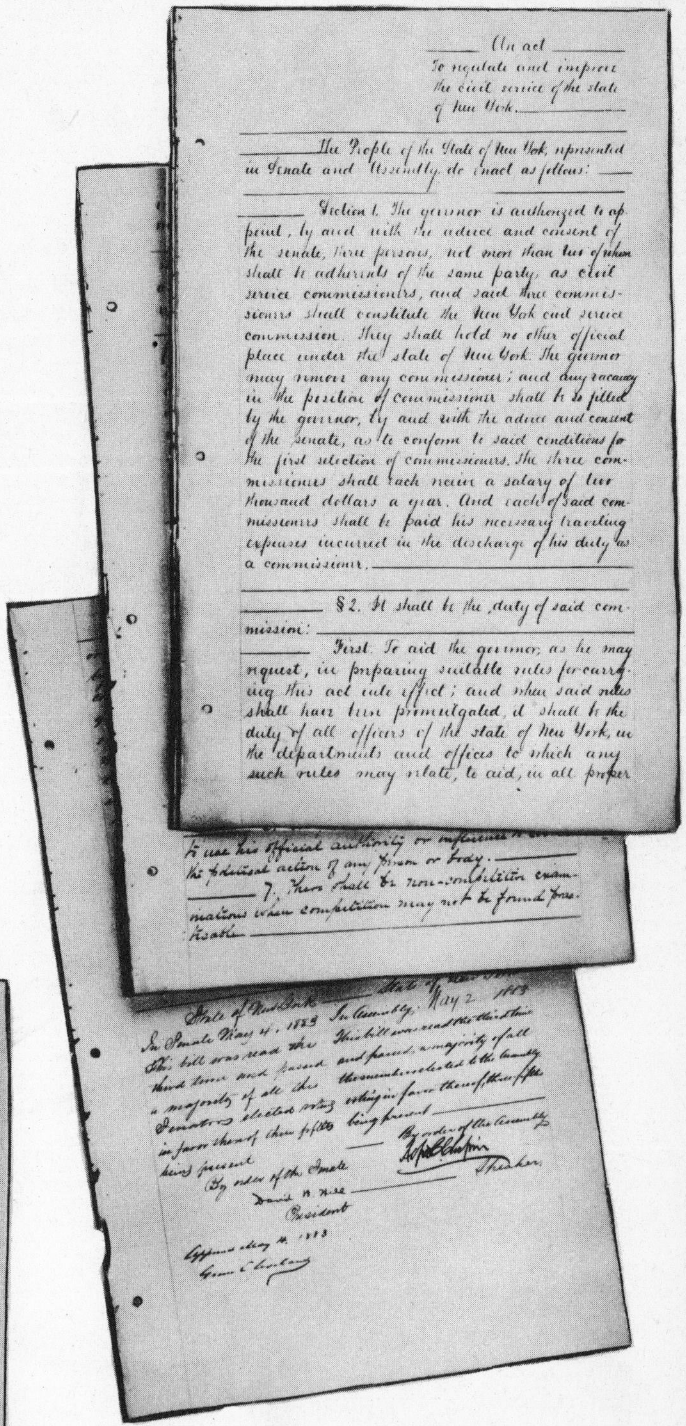

An act

To regulate and improve the civil service of the state of New York.

The People of the State of New York, represented in Senate and Assembly, do enact as follows:

Section 1. The governor is authorized to appoint, by and with the advice and consent of the senate, three persons, not more than two of whom shall be adherents of the same party, as civil service commissioners, and said three commissioners shall constitute the New York civil service commission. They shall hold no other official place under the state of New York. The governor may remove any commissioner; and any vacancy in the position of commissioner shall be so filled by the governor, by and with the advice and consent of the senate, as to conform to said conditions for the first selection of commissioners. The three commissioners shall each receive a salary of two thousand dollars a year. And each of said commissioners shall be paid his necessary traveling expenses incurred in the discharge of his duty as a commissioner.

§ 2. It shall be the duty of said commission:

First. To aid the governor, as he may request, in preparing suitable rules for carrying this act into effect; and when said rules shall have been promulgated, it shall be the duty of all officers of the state of New York, in the departments and offices to which any such rules may relate, to aid, in all proper

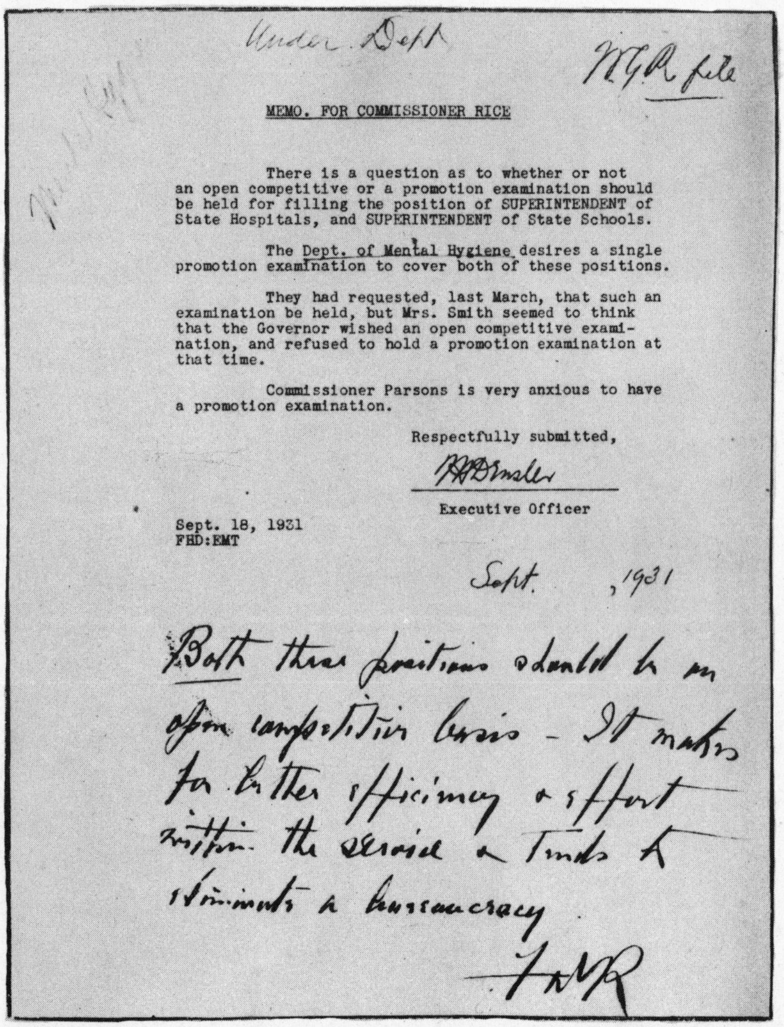

Under Dept

MEMO. FOR COMMISSIONER RICE

There is a question as to whether or not an open competitive or a promotion examination should be held for filling the position of SUPERINTENDENT of State Hospitals, and SUPERINTENDENT of State Schools.

The Dept. of Mental Hygiene desires a single promotion examination to cover both of these positions.

They had requested, last March, that such an examination be held, but Mrs. Smith seemed to think that the Governor wished an open competitive examination, and refused to hold a promotion examination at that time.

Commissioner Parsons is very anxious to have a promotion examination.

Respectfully submitted,

Executive Officer

Sept. 18, 1931
FHD:EMT

Sept. , 1931

Both these positions should be on open competitive basis - It makes for better efficiency & effort within the service & tends to eliminate a bureaucracy

FDR

To protect the civil service worker from political abuse, to achieve greater efficiency, New York passed the first CIVIL SERVICE LAW in the country, May 4, 1883 (shown above).

Governor Franklin D. Roosevelt, in a MEMORANDUM (at left) September, 1931, stood for open competitive civil service examinations as . . . *"It makes for better efficiency and effort . . . ."*

Senate, No. 2651

Assembly, No. 2765

CHAP. 468

AN ACT

To amend the labor law, in relation to creating an unemployment insurance fund and providing for the method and mode of its administration, and making an appropriation to carry out the provisions thereof

The People of the State of New York, represented in Senate and Assembly, do enact as follows:

Section 1. Article eighteen and sections five hundred to five hundred and five, inclusive, of chapter fifty of the laws of nineteen hundred twenty-one, entitled "An act in relation to labor, constituting chapter thirty-one of the consolidated laws," as such article and sections were so renumbered by chapter four hundred and five of the laws of nineteen hundred twenty-two, are hereby renumbered, respectively, article twenty and sections six hundred to six hundred and five, inclusive, and such chapter is hereby

STATE OF NEW YORK
EXECUTIVE CHAMBER
ALBANY

April 25, 1935.

MEMORANDUM filed with Assembly Bill Introductory Number 1, Senate Reprint Number 2651, entitled:

"AN ACT to amend the labor law, in relation to creating an unemployment insurance fund and providing for the method and mode of its administration, and making an appropriation to carry out the provisions thereof"

A P P R O V E D

I am most happy to append my signature to this bill which establishes unemployment insurance for the working people of the State of New York. For three years I have repeatedly recommended to the Legislature the passage of such a bill. And so, I am very pleased to be able to place this law permanently upon the statute books of our State.

In my mind it stands out as the most progressive and enlightened piece of social legislation enacted in this State in many decades. The people of the State of New York should feel proud that it is once again leading the Nation in legislation which will increase the economic and moral security of its working people, cushion the hardships of economic depressions, and advance the general well-being.

The bill is approved.

Herbert H. Lehman

Assembly, No. 1138

CHAP. 118

AN ACT

To amend the executive law, in relation to prevention and elimination of practices of discrimination in employment and otherwise against persons because of race, creed, color or national origin, creating in the executive department a state commission against discrimination, defining its functions, powers and duties and providing for the appointment and compensation of its officers and employees

The People of the State of New York, represented in Senate and Assembly, do enact as follows:

Section 1. Chapter twenty-three of the laws of nineteen hundred nine, entitled "An act in relation to executive officers, constituting chapter eighteen of the consolidated laws," is hereby amended by inserting therein, after article eleven, a new article, to be article twelve, to read as follows:

because of race, creed, color or national origin, either by employers, labor organizations, employment agencies or other persons, and to take other actions against discrimination because of race, creed, color or national origin, as herein provided; and the commission established hereunder is hereby given general jurisdiction and power for such purposes.

§ 126. Opportunity for employment without discrimination a civil right. The opportunity to obtain employment without discrimination because of race, creed, color or national origin is hereby recognized as and declared to be a civil right.

§ 127. Definitions. When used in this article: 1. The term "person" includes one or more individuals, partnerships, associations, corporations, legal representatives, trustees, trustees in bankruptcy, or receivers.

2. The term "employment agency" includes any person undertaking to procure employees or opportunities to work.

3. The term "labor organization" includes any organization which exists and is constituted for the purpose, in whole or in part, of collective bargaining or of dealing with employers concerning grievances, terms or conditions of employment, or of other mutual aid or protection in connection with employment.

The term "unlawful employment practice" includes only unlawful employment practices specified in section one hundred forty-one of this article.

The term "employer" does not include a club exclusively fraternal, charitable, educational or religious association or corporation, if such club, association or corporation is not

14

If any clause, sentence, paragraph or part . . . application thereof to any person or circumstance . . . reason, be adjudged by a court of competent . . . invalid, such judgment shall not affect, impair, . . . remainder of this article.

. . . article twelve of the laws of nineteen hundred forty-one . . . fifty-four of the laws of nineteen hundred . . . bered by chapter five of the laws of nineteen hundred . . . section one hundred forty-four having been amended . . . two hundred sixteen of the laws of nineteen hundred . . . two, is hereby renumbered article twelve-a.

This act shall take effect July first, nineteen hundred forty-two.

Approved,

Thomas E. Dewey

March 12, 1945.

The above signature is genuine but was written with 22 different pens and therefore differs from the usual signature in appearance.

Thomas E. Dewey

Freedom

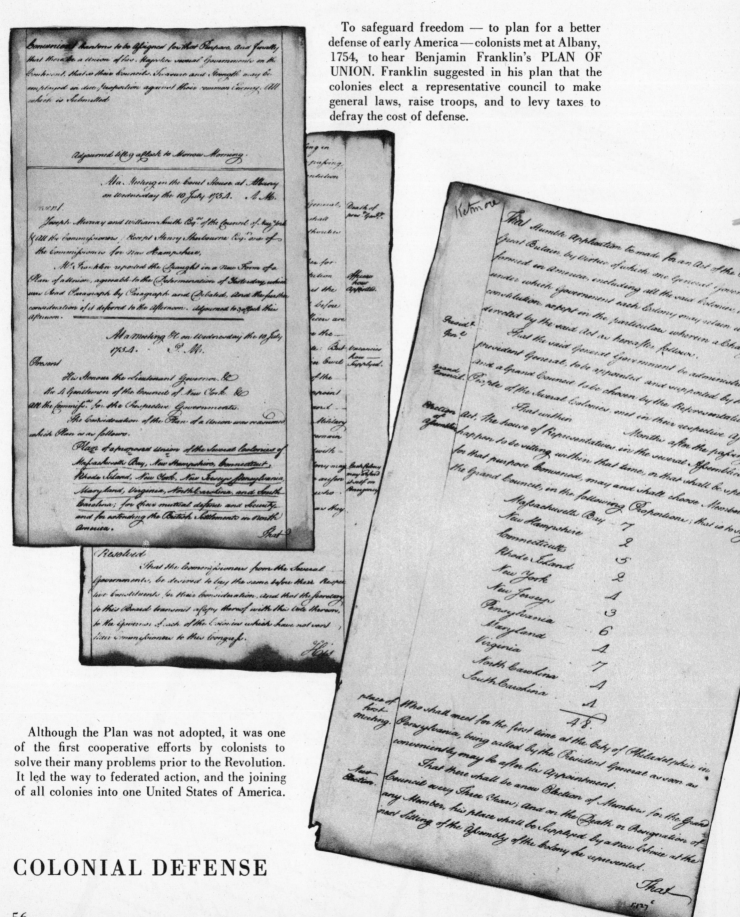

To safeguard freedom — to plan for a better defense of early America — colonists met at Albany, 1754, to hear Benjamin Franklin's PLAN OF UNION. Franklin suggested in his plan that the colonies elect a representative council to make general laws, raise troops, and to levy taxes to defray the cost of defense.

Although the Plan was not adopted, it was one of the first cooperative efforts by colonists to solve their many problems prior to the Revolution. It led the way to federated action, and the joining of all colonies into one United States of America.

COLONIAL DEFENSE

Protected...

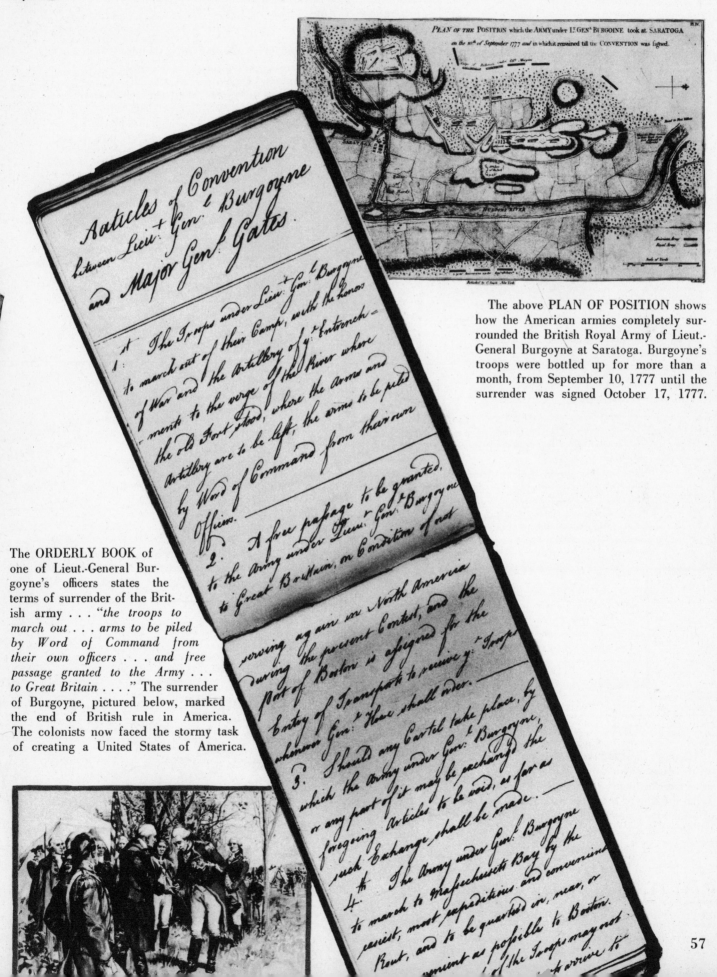

The above PLAN OF POSITION shows how the American armies completely surrounded the British Royal Army of Lieut.-General Burgoyne at Saratoga. Burgoyne's troops were bottled up for more than a month, from September 10, 1777 until the surrender was signed October 17, 1777.

The ORDERLY BOOK of one of Lieut.-General Burgoyne's officers states the terms of surrender of the British army . . . "*the troops to march out . . . arms to be piled by Word of Command from their own officers . . . and free passage granted to the Army . . . to Great Britain . . . .*" The surrender of Burgoyne, pictured below, marked the end of British rule in America. The colonists now faced the stormy task of creating a United States of America.

Freedom Protected...

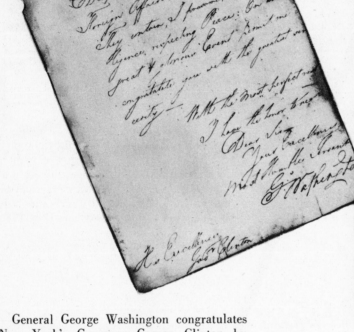

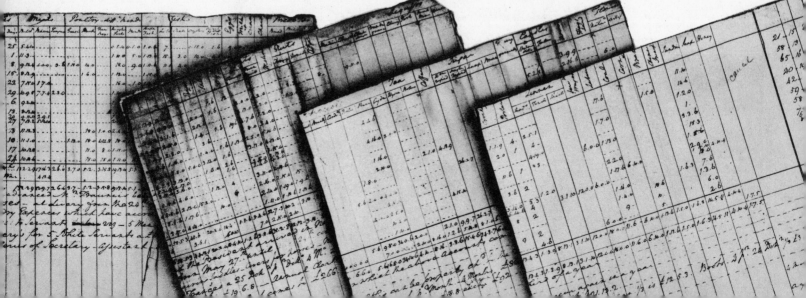

New-York, Nov. 24, 1783.

The Committee appointed to conduct the Order of receiving their Excellencies Governor CLINTON and General WASHINGTON,

BEG Leave to inform their Fellow-Citizens, that the Troops, under the Command of Major-General KNOX, will take Possession of the City at the Hour agreed on, Tuesday next ; as soon as this may be performed, he will request the Citizens who may be assembled on Horseback, at the Bowling-Green, the lower End of the Broad-Way, to accompany him to meet their Excellencies Governor CLINTON and General WASHINGTON, at the Bull's Head, in the Bowery---the Citizens on Foot to assemble at or near the Tea-water-Pump at Fresh-water.

ORDER OF PROCESSION.

A Party of Horse will precede their Excellencies and be on their flanks---after the General and Governor, will follow the Lieutenant-Governor and Members of the Council for the temporary Government of the Southern Parts of the State---The Gentlemen on Horse-back, eight in Front---those on Foot, in the Rear of the Horse, in like Manner. Their Excellencies, after passing down Queen-Street, and the Line of Troops up the Broadway, will a-light at CAPE's Tavern.

The Committee hope to see their Fellow-Citizens, conduct themselves with Decency and Decorum on this joyful Occasion.

CITIZENS TAKE CARE!!!

THE Inhabitants are hereby informed, that Permission has been obtained from the Commandant, to form themselves in patroles this night, and that every order requisite will be given to the guards, as well to aid and assist, as to give protection to the patroles: And that the countersign will be given to THOMAS TUCKER, No. 51, Water-Street; from whom it can be obtained, if necessary.

It is requested that such of the Inhabitants who are not on the patroles, and sickness does not prevent, will keep themselves awake.

It is also desired, for the sake of order, that the Gentlemen who have been heretofore appointed to superintend the nightly watches, to call their districts together at an early hour.

NEW-YORK: PRINTED BY SAMUEL LOUDON.

General George Washington congratulates New York's Governor George Clinton by LETTER, 1783, when peace was declared at end of the Revolutionary War.

The above BROADSIDE, November 24, 1783, gives order of triumphal parade planned by New Yorkers welcoming Clinton and Washington to the City at close of Revolutionary War.

Below, is the household EXPENSE RECORD Washington kept during his first year, 1789, as President. Residing in New York City, which was then the Capitol, Washington accepted only expenses, no salary.

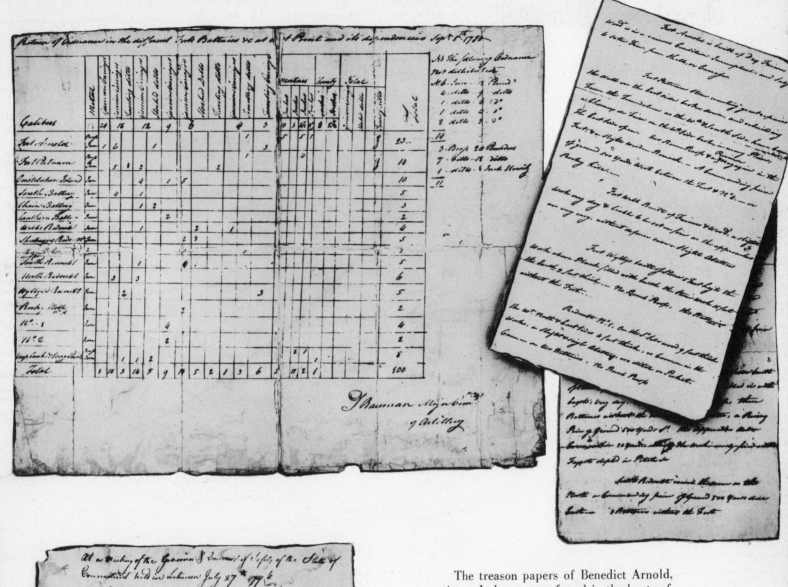

The treason papers of Benedict Arnold, pictured above, were found in the boots of Major John Andre when he was captured after visiting Arnold at West Point. They are DESCRIPTION OF WORKS at West Point, in Arnold's handwriting, and RETURN OF ORDNANCE, listing the Point's forts and batteries, September 5, 1780.

John Jay, left, borrows 20 cannon for New York from Connecticut Governor Trumbull. Below, Westchester County's Committee of Safety assures the Provincial Committee of Safety . . . *"of loyal support."*

Freedom Protected...

Washington spent long hours writing his 19-page FAREWELL ADDRESS, which was published in September, 1796, six months before he left office. Helped by Hamilton, Washington explained what he had done as President, set forth those principles of good government America might wisely follow, saying . . . "*Observe good faith and justice toward all nations. Cultivate peace and harmony with all . . . .*" Significant passages from this Address are shown below and on the opposite page.

(1)

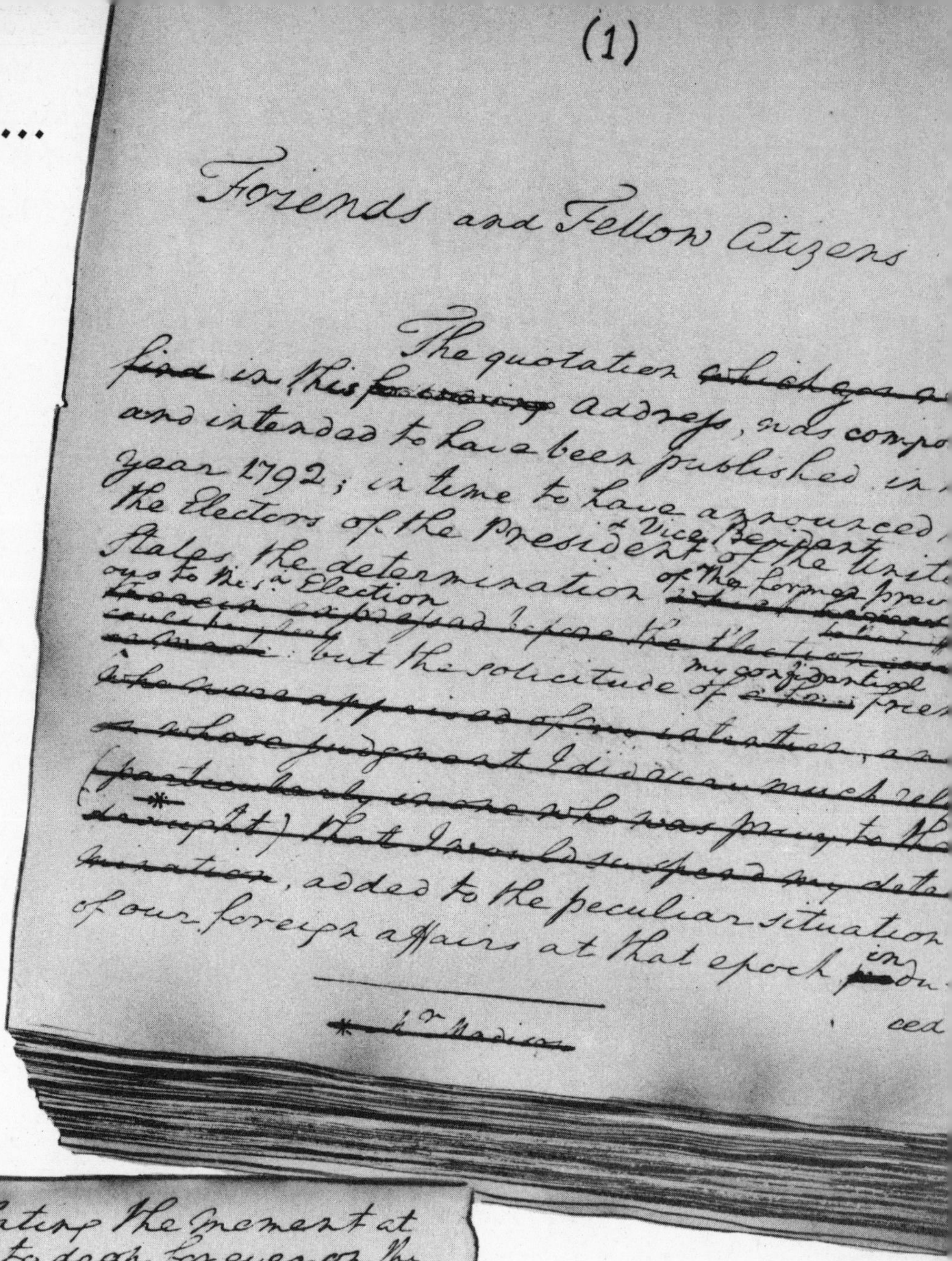

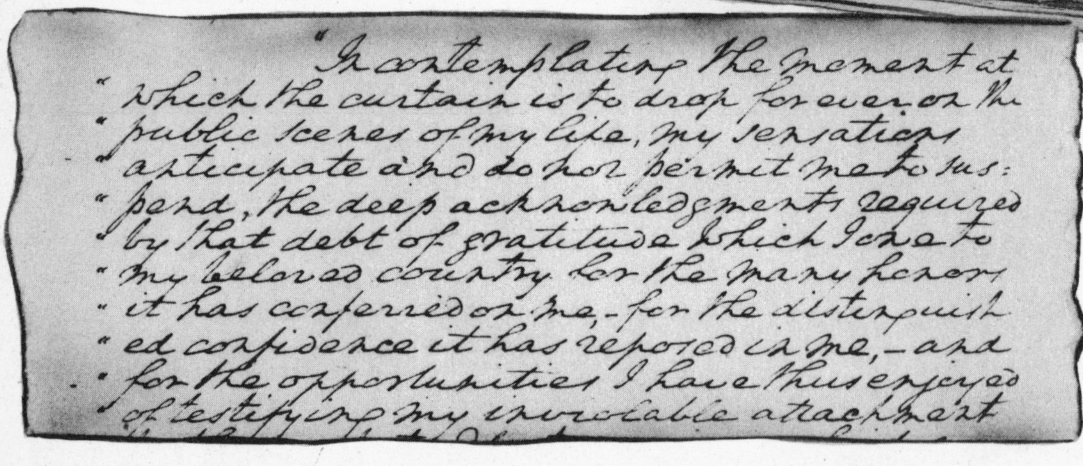

Friends and Fellow Citizens

The quotation ... in this ... address, was compo...
and intended to have been published in ...
year 1792; in time to have announced, ...
the Electors of the President & Vice President of the Unite...
States, the determination of the former previous to the 1st Election ...
... but the solicitude of my confidential friend ...
..., added to the peculiar situation
of our foreign affairs at that epoch in-du-
ced

"In contemplating the moment at
"which the curtain is to drop forever on the
"public scenes of my life, my sensations
"anticipate and do not permit me to sus-
"pend, the deep acknowledgments required
"by that debt of gratitude which I owe to
"my beloved country for the many honors
"it has conferred on me,—for the distinguish-
"ed confidence it has reposed in me,—and
"for the opportunities I have thus enjoyed
"of testifying my inviolable attachment

Washington expressed . . . "*a debt of gratitude which I owe to my beloved country. . . .*"

"the guardian of our common rights—and
"the patron of our common interests—and
"wisely containing within itself a provisi-
"on for its own amendment, as experience
"may point out its errors, seems to promise
"every thing that can be expected from such
"an institution;—and if supported by wise
"Councils—by virtuous conduct—and by mu-
"tual and friendly allowances, must approach
"as near to perfection as any human work
can

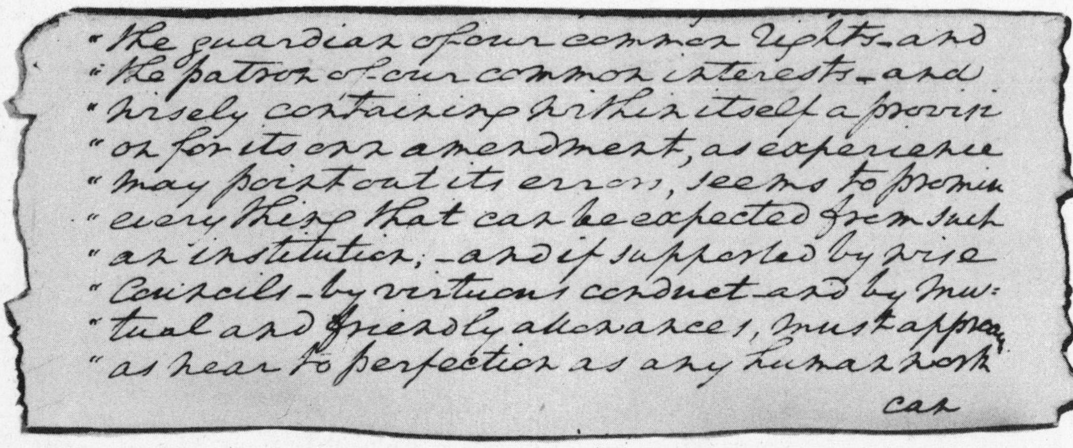

The Constitution, which had so recently been adopted, Washington found workable. He thought it approached . . . "*perfection.*"

He cautioned young America to fulfil . . . "*all engagements* . . ." because "*honesty will forever be found to be the best policy.*"

That we may fulfil with the greatest exactitude all our engagements: foreign and domestic, to the utmost of our abilities whensoever, and in whatsoever manner they are pledged: for in public, as in private life, I am persuaded that honesty will be found to be the best policy

Washington did not believe this country should be involved with foreign nations. Such alliances could lead only to war.

will ultimately terminate — but easy indeed is it to foresee that it may involve us in disputes, and finally in War, to fulfil political alliances. — Whereas, if there be no engagement on

America was to . . . "*never unsheath the sword except in self-defense.*" Washington prophesied that if this nation could remain at peace for 20 years it need fear no other worldly power.

sound policy and our essential Interests. —
That we may be always prepared for War, but never unsheath the sword except in self defence so long as Justice and our essential rights, and national respectibility can be preserved without it — for without

He warned public servants of their trust; also cautioned the people to keep faith in their government.

the measure. — If public servants, in the exercise of their official duties, are found incompetent or pursuing wrong courses discontinue them. — If they are guilty of mal' practices in office, let them be more exemplarily punished — in both cases the Constitution & Laws have made provision, but do not withdraw your confidence from them — the

Bidding farewell to his people, Washington closed his Address, saying . . . "*I leave you with undefiled hands — an uncorrupted heart. . . .*"

(19)

been blessed amidst the tumult, which have harrassed other countries. — I leave you with undefiled hands — an uncorrupted heart — and with ardent vows to heaven for the Welfare & happiness of that country in which I, and my forefathers to the third or fourth Ancestry drew our first breath. —

G.º Washington

Freedom Protected...

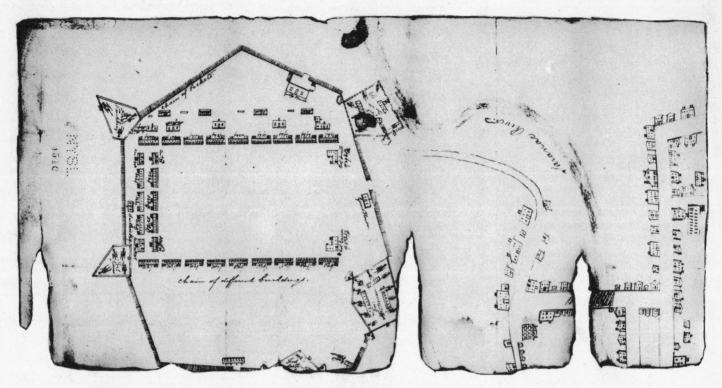

SKETCH of the Plattsburgh cantonment above, shows buildings, pickets and other defenses.

CONTRACT between Governor John Jay and Builders Hooker and Putman calls for an arsenal at Albany.

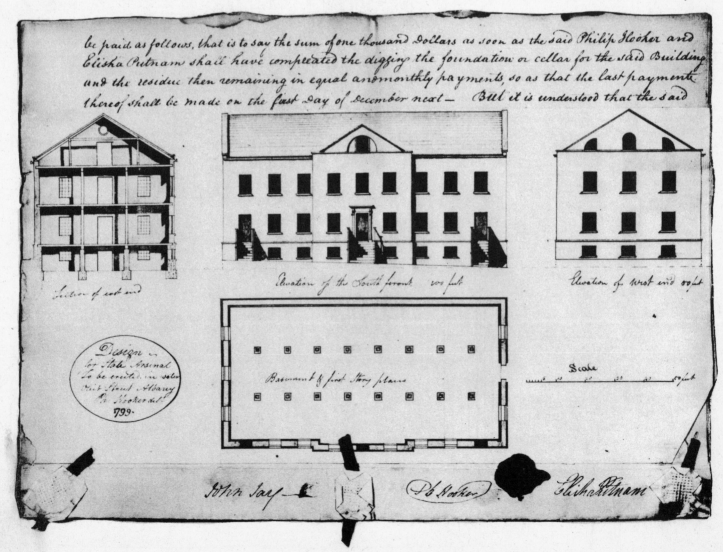

Yankee General, calling for Volunteers by sounding the Trumpet.

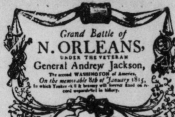
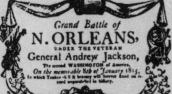

Grand Battle of N. ORLEANS,
UNDER THE VETERAN
General Andrew Jackson,
The second WASHINGTON of America, On the memorable 8th of January, 1815, In which Yankee skill & bravery will forever stand on record unparalleled in history.

UNITED WE STAND; DIVIDED—WE FALL.

A British General, surrounded and taken by Yankee light horse.

Gen. Drummond attempts to escape by the fleetness of a Bear, but is surrounded and taken prisoner.

Lord Castlereagh, mounted on a Goat, in the attitude of delivering his late "Sine qua non" to the British ministers at Ghent.

Interesting Sketch.
Extracts of Letters—Official.

New-Orleans, Jan 13, 1815.

General Brisbane, on a quick retreat, in irritation of a Monkey on a Pig.

BATTLE OF PLATTSBURGH,
AND
VICTORY on LAKE CHAMPLAIN,

In which 14,000 British myrmidons were defeated and put to flight by 5,000 Yankees and Green-mountain Boys, on the memorable Eleventh of Sept. 1814.

Tune—"Battle of the Kegs."

Sir George Prevost with all his host
Much'd forth from Montreal, Sir,
Both he and they as blithe and gay
As going to a ball, Sir.

BRITISH LION.

M'DONOUGH'S SHIP.

COLUMBIA, represented as surrounded by enemies.

Battle of Niagara!
OR,
AMERICA again victorious over her white and red savage Enemies!

British Colonel in a fright, Lest his bat in the fight, Running off in the night, What a laughable sight!

A Cossack, smoaking his pipe & thumping his Mule with a cudgel to keep up with the rest.

Lieutenant-Col. Everet, To keep up fame and files, Upon a Camel mounts And off in haste he rides!

CAPT. DOWNIE.

The valiant Major Bright, Astride the Goat pursues, And hastes to Montreal, To tell the horrid news!

A French Canadian, retreating on an Ass, & whipping up for dear life.

A Green-Mountain Boy, with his foot on the head of an Indian.

COMMODORE MACDONOUGH's VICTORY.

O FREEMEN, raise a joyous strain!
Aloft the Eagle towers,
"We're met the enemy" again—
Again have made them 'OURS!'

The Indian Chief so bent o prey, Of Infant scalping who can tell The horrors of that dire day, Where echo groans with savage yell?

A Vermonter, attacking the veterans of Lord Wellington, while crossing the fatal river.

The feeling Mistress follows her husband to the field of battle, whilst flames and cruelties at Hampton, Havre-de-Grace, and the River Rasin!

GENIUS of AMERICA in Combat with OLD JONNY BULL.

GEN MACOMB.
GOV. PREVOST.
GENIUS of AMERICA in Combat with OLD JONNY BULL.

COLUMBIA, claiming victorious over all her enemies—reclining in Peace, and surrounded with plenty

WINDSOR, (Vt.)
Printed for the Flying Book-Sellers, Jan. 1, 1815.

The news of Champlain The Prince Regent receives; He mounts his old Bull, 'It bit too, he doth pull, And, frantic with sadness, Most bitterly grieves.

Gov. Gen. of the Canadas arrested for cowardice, and seated on an Elephant.

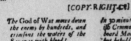

The God of War moves down the enemy by hundreds, and crimson the waters of the Saranac with blood!

In 30 minutes, said the British Commodore, I will be on board Macdonough's ship; but behold him slain the first fire, and his ship a wreck!

A few British Gun Boats barely escape to carry the dismal tidings of defeat and destruction of their fleet.

With pain and woe, Death strikes the foe A heavy blow, And lays him low.

[COPY-RIGHT.]

Impressive BROADSIDE, September, 1814, tells of the Battle of Plattsburgh.
This battle won for America freedom of the seas and security for her sailors.

63

Ceremonies Attending the Arrival of the New York State Freedom Train in Rochester, March 18, 1949.

NEW YORK STATE'S FREEDOM TRAIN

Described by
DR. CHARLES FRANCIS GOSNELL
NEW YORK STATE LIBRARIAN AND
ASSISTANT COMMISSIONER OF EDUCATION

The New York State Freedom Train originated in the great rotunda of the New York State Library, in November 1947, when the National Freedom Train stopped in Albany. The National Train was scheduled for a stop of only one day, and many were unable to see it. For those who did get on, there was very little about their home state. So Edna L. Jacobsen, associate librarian and head of the Manuscripts and History Section of the State Library, assembled an exhibition of books and documents with two objectives: to duplicate where possible the items on the train, and to tell the full story of New York State's contribution to the growth of freedom.

The exhibit proved so popular that The Knickerbocker News of Albany ran a series of ten articles on it. Then Gerald H. Salisbury, editor of The Knickerbocker News, proposed that the exhibit be put on wheels to be sent all through the State. The New York Society of Newspaper Editors and the State Publishers Association gave their support to the proposal. The State Legislature passed a bill to create a commis-

sion and appropriate $50,000 toward expenses of the setting-up of the train. Governor Dewey was enthusiastic in support of the project and appointed five members to the Commission, including Mr. Salisbury as chairman, and the State Librarian, Dr. Charles Francis Gosnell, as Secretary.

Officials of the New York Central were cordially cooperative, and work on the cars was begun in September 1948. Plans were developed by members of the commission with the aid of Stanley G. Somers and Arthur Kimberly, who had helped on the National Train the year before, and Herman F. Robinton, administrative assistant to the State Librarian.

Working drawings and all shopwork were completed in the New York Central shops at Albany. Lucite plastic cases for the documents were made by Victor S. Clark of Flushing.

The role of New York State in the historic evolution of American freedom has been an active one. The Colony of New Netherland, and later New York, was the focal point for many of the struggles for freedom in colonial days. As a state, New York has usually been in the vanguard of reform. In its archives, in the New York State Library at Albany, the State has a great treasure of original manuscripts which serve as milestones marking the road to freedom.

The exhibits are grouped with documents on *Freedom of Expression* in Car 1, those on *Liberty under Law* in Car 2 and those on *Freedom of Self-Development* in Car 3.

There are 84 documents in all, of which ten were borrowed from private sources or local institutions.

The earliest documents come from the official archives of the Dutch governors of New Netherland. One of the strongest testimonies to the desire for religious freedom came to Governor Peter Stuyvesant from Flushing, Long Island, in 1657. The Flushing Remonstrance was the answer to an official ban on Quakers. Despite threats of imprisonment and banishment, 26 freeholders of the Town of Flushing defiantly signed the Remonstrance, protesting the injustice inflicted on the Quakers.

Following the advent of the British representatives of the Duke of York, later King James II, the colonists won the Duke's Laws of 1665, and the Charter of Libertyes and Priviledges of 1683. This charter was notable for providing a representative assembly whose consent was necessary for the imposition of new taxes.

Freedom of the Press is well illustrated by copies of the New York Weekly Journal of 1734 and the complaint of his attorneys, from the press of John Peter Zenger. His actual arrest "for printing seditious libells" is illustrated by the manuscript minutes of the New York Executive Council.

The evolution of constitutional government is shown by a series beginning with the first New York State Constitution, written hurriedly at Kingston in 1777 by a harried band of patriots. It is followed by the Minutes of the Poughkeepsie Convention of 1788 called to consider the new Federal Constitution. After lengthy and bitter debate New York State ratified the Federal Constitution by a vote of 31 to 29, insisting on a number of amendments which were later included in the Bill of Rights, and one long-forgot, a "no third term for president." Many reforms were embodied in the Constitution of 1846, which soon became a model for many western states.

New York State leadership in abolishing racial discrimination is documented beginning with the abolition of Indian slavery in 1679, Negro slavery in 1799, up to the anti-discrimination laws of 1945 and 1948. Also included is the original manuscript by Abraham Lincoln of the Emancipation Proclamation of September 22, 1862, which the State Library acquired in 1865.

The story of labor extends from accounts of union activities in 1675 down to the unemployment insurance law of 1935.

Included in the series on women's rights are manuscripts in the handwriting of Amelia Bloomer, Susan B. Anthony and Mary E. Walker. The importance of mobility in the development of the State is indicated by references to the Erie Canal, the beginnings of the New York Central Railroad and the westward movement of immigrants.

Inspiration to constructive patriotism is furnished by the manuscript of George Washington's Farewell Address acquired by the State Library in 1871, accounts of the battles of Saratoga and Plattsburg, the papers found in the boots of the spy Major André and the original draft by Francis Bellamy of the Pledge of Allegiance to the Flag.

Opportunity for self-development and the building of an enlightened citizenry through education have been primary concerns in New York State from colonial days down to the present. Nine documents in the New York State Freedom Train point milestones in the history of education in the State and emphasize the great importance attached to the concept of education for all.

The Train consisted of six cars prepared especially by the New York Central Railroad in its Albany car shops. Three electrically air-conditioned New York Central passenger cars were remodeled to contain the exhibit cases. All windows were covered with steel plates inside and out, and an automatic carbon-dioxide fire-extinguishing system and burglar alarm were installed. The steel exhibition cases were arranged to facilitate movement through the cars and also to permit lecturers or teachers to conduct large groups and direct their attention to groups of documents. The cases were provided with shatter-proof glass and fluorescent lighting, and were located on alternate sides of the cars so that a visitor passing through would not have to look at both sides at once. Inside the cases each book or document was inclosed in its own tight plastic case, together with a descriptive label.

A fourth car served as office and passenger car for personnel. A fifth car, lent by the Pennsylvania Railroad, was a combination baggage and passenger car for baggage and railroad personnel. Electric power for operating the lighting, air-conditioning and other appliances was supplied by a power car containing a new installation of Diesel-electric generators.

The six cars were painted bright blue and gold—the official New York State colors—and carry bronze castings of the New York State seal on each side. The letter-board bears the words "New York State Freedom Train" in bold gold letters.

The train was formerly put into commission at Albany by Governor Thomas E. Dewey on January 26, 1949 and ran to capacity crowds all through the year, stopping in every city, and stopping long enough for all to see their State's most precious possessions.

NEW YORK STATE FREEDOM TRAIN

LIST OF EXHIBITS

CAR I. FREEDOM OF EXPRESSION

CASE 1. FREEDOM OF RELIGION

RELIGIOUS FREEDOM FOR OTHER PEOPLE. June 6, 1641. Freedom of religion was one of the privileges granted to the English colonists who had been permitted by the Dutch authorities to settle in New Netherland. (Written in the Dutch language.) N. Y. Colonial Manuscripts, v. 4, p. 93. See sect. 2. (No. 1) From the State Library, Albany.

FLUSHING REMONSTRANCE. December 27, 1657. A protest by the freeholders of Flushing and Jamaica, Long Island, living under the rule of the Dutch, to Governor Peter Stuyvesant, because he had forbidden Quakers living among them to hold religious meetings. This was a violation by the Dutch Governor of the Flushing Charter of 1645 which guaranteed freedom of religion to all the inhabitants of the settlements. This petition has been called the first "American Declaration of Independence." N. Y. Colonial Manuscripts, v. 3, p. 626-627. (No. 2) From the State Library, Albany.

GOVERNOR STUYVESANT REBUKED. April 16, 1663. Dutch Governor Peter Stuyvesant arrested John Bowne, a Flushing Quaker, who persisted in holding religious meetings in his home. Bowne was banished and went to Holland for a hearing before the Directors of the West India Company. The Directors released him and rebuked the headstrong governor. The Directors wrote Governor Stuyvesant that he should "at least not force people's consciences, but allow everyone to have his own belief, as long as he behaves quietly and legally, gives no offence to his neighbors and does not oppose the government." (Document in the Dutch language.) N. Y. Colonial Manuscripts, v. 15, p. 12. (No. 3) From the State Library, Albany.

RELIGIOUS FREEDOM FOR LUTHERANS. September 26, 1673. Dutch Governor Anthony Colve grants Lutheran congregation in Albany free exercise of their religion. (Document in the Dutch language.) N. Y. Colonial Manuscripts, v. 23, p. 86-87. (No. 4) From the State Library, Albany.

CHARTER OF LIBERTIES AND PRIVILEGES. Passed by the first New York Legislature, October 30, 1683. The English Colonial Governor, Colonel Thomas Dongan, a Catholic, extended to the colony among other important rights, freedom of religion. This provision was included in substance in Section 38 of the Constitution of 1777. (No. 5) Lent by Town of North Hempstead.

NEW YORK'S FIRST STATE CONSTITUTION. 1777. Provided the framework of state and local government. Section 38, here shown, specified religious liberty for all in no uncertain terms. Written at Kingston, with the British invasion threatening, a group of young patriots worked hard to finish the Constitution. John Jay, the chief author, was 30 years old, and he was assisted in the main by Robert Livingston, age 26, and Gouverneur Morris, age 24. (No. 6) From the State Library, Albany.

CASE 2. FREEDOM OF PRESS AND SPEECH

JOHN PETER ZENGER'S *NEW YORK WEEKLY JOURNAL*. 1734. Zenger published in his JOURNAL attacks upon the English Colonial Governor William Cosby and his party. A sample: "The people of New York think, as matters now stand, that their liberties and properties are precarious, and that slavery is likely to be entailed on them and their posterity, if some past things be not amended." The copies of the JOURNAL were ordered burned, and Zenger was imprisoned for criminal libel. (No. 7) From the State Library, Albany.

JOHN PETER ZENGER'S *NEW YORK WEEKLY JOURNAL*. 1734-35. No. 55, November 25, 1734, published under Zenger's direction from prison. No. 48, September 30, 1734, one of the issues that led to Zenger's prosecution for libel and the vindication of freedom of the press in America. No. 93, August 18, 1735, published after Zenger's trial, in which he gave his first account of the proceedings. (No. 7A) Lent by New York Historical Society, New York City.

JOHN PETER ZENGER ARRESTED. 1734. The New York Executive Council ordered Zenger's arrest "for printing and publishing several seditious libells dispersed throughout his Journalls or Newspapers." Minutes of Council shown. N. Y. Council Minutes, v. 17, p. 25. (No. 8) From the State Library, Albany.

COMPLAINT OF ZENGER'S COUNSEL. December 27, 1735. The English Colonial Governor William Cosby disbarred the lawyers who dared to defend Zenger. In this document the lawyers declare that their disbarment was contrary to the provision of the Magna Carta, "We will deny no man, we will delay to no Man, Justice or Right." Andrew Hamilton of Philadelphia, the greatest lawyer in the colonies, volunteered to act for the defense. It was proven that Zenger's statements were true, and he was quickly acquitted by the jury. His acquittal established in New York and the colonies the principle of freedom of the press and of speech. (No. 9) From the State Library, Albany.

THE TRIAL OF PETER ZENGER OF NEW-YORK, PRINTER, WHO WAS TRIED AND ACQUITTED, FOR PRINTING AND PUBLISHING A LIBEL AGAINST THE GOVERNMENT, WITH THE PLEADINGS AND ARGUMENT ON BOTH SIDES. London, 1752. The trial took place in 1735. (No. 10) From the State Library, Albany.

LIBERTY OF THE PRESS DEFENDED. *An essay on the liberty of the press*, by George Hay. Philadelphia, 1799. An influential publication which argued that "The freedom of the press . . . means the total exemption of the press from any kind of control, and consequently the sedition bill, which is an act of legislative control, is an abridgement of its liberty, and expressly forbidden by the Constitution." (No. 11) From the State Library, Albany.

ARBITRARY GOVERNMENT PROTESTED. December 11, 1653. Protest of delegates from New Amsterdam and Long Island towns, under Dutch rule, meeting in convention at City Hall, New Amsterdam, against "arbitrary government." The principle of government by consent of the governed is asserted in this protest of delegates. The delegates said to Governor Stuyvesant and his Council that " 'Tis contrary to the first intentions and genuine principles of every well regulated government, that one or more men should arrogate to themselves the exclusive power to dispose, at will, of the life and property of any individual, and this, by virtue or under pretense of a law or order he, or they, might enact, without the consent, knowledge or election of the whole Body, or its agents or representatives." (Document in the Dutch language.) N. Y. Colonial Manuscripts, v. 5, p. 160, 162. (No. 12) From the State Library, Albany.

CHARTER OF LIBERTIES AND PRIVILEGES. 1683. ("Dongan's Laws") The supreme legislative authority in the colony was vested in a Governor, Council, and "The People met in General Assembly" to be called at least once every three years. No taxes could be imposed without the Assembly's consent. This charter stands as the pioneer among charters or constitutions in America conferring on the people the right of representative government. (No. 13) From the State Library, Albany.

NEW YORK COLONIAL COUNCIL. April 9, 1691. The Colonial Legislature consisted of a Council appointed by the Governor and a House of Representatives elected by the people. In these minutes of the first meeting, James Graham, Speaker of the House, is authorized to address the Council. N. Y. Council Minutes, Legislative, v. 6, p. 1. (No. 14) From the State Library, Albany.

NEW YORK COLONIAL REPRESENTATIVES. April 9, 1691. Order of House of Representatives for Speaker to address the Council on the rights and privileges of the House. N. Y. Colonial Manuscripts, v. 37, p. 98a. (No. 15) From the State Library, Albany.

COXSACKIE DECLARATION OF INDEPENDENCE. May 17, 1775. This "general association" was signed by 225 citizens of Coxsackie who agreed to execute the recommendations of the Continental Congress and those to be made by the New York Provincial Congress in order to save "the rights and liberties of America" and to preserve "our Constitution." This precedes the Mecklenburg, North Carolina, Declaration of May 20, 1775, and also that of the national, or Jefferson's Declaration of July 2, 1776, now commemorated on Independence Day, July 4. (No. 16) Lent by the Albany Institute of History and Art.

CIVIL POWER DECLARED SUPERIOR TO THE MILITARY. March 1, 1776. New York delegates to the Continental Congress assert that except in extreme emergency civil power is superior to that of the military. In this letter to the New York Provincial Convention, Lewis Morris, later one of the signers of the Declaration of Independence, James Duane, John Alsop, and John Jay explain their conduct in protesting the action of General Charles Lee in imposing loyalty test on inhabitants of New York Colony. (No. 17) From the State Library, Albany.

NEW YORK'S SECOND STATE CONSTITUTION. 1821. This Constitution abolished the Council of Revision which was a practical oligarchy. It also provided a method for the Legislature to override the Governor's veto. (No. 18) From the State Library, Albany.

"ORDERLY SELF-GOVERNING LIBERTY" FOR THE PHILIPPINES. December 17, 1901. Advocated by Theodore Roosevelt as President of the United States in a letter to the Reverend Edward Everett Hale. Finally achieved by President Truman's Proclamation, July 4, 1946. (No. 19) From the State Library, Albany.

THEODORE ROOSEVELT'S *ROUGH RIDERS*. May 1, 1899. Part of the original manuscript, including the Dedication, dated from the Executive Mansion, Albany, May 1, 1899, when Roosevelt was Governor of New York State. Colonel Roosevelt commanded the "Rough Riders" who gained fame in the liberation of Cuba in the War with Spain, 1898. (No. 20) From the State Library, Albany.

CASE 4. LABOR RIGHTS

"DUKE'S LAWS." 1665-1691. Earliest of English colonial laws enacted in convention at Hempstead, Long Island, 1665. A section on *Masters, Servants, and Labourers* sets forth in detail the legal protection from harsh masters. Constables and overseers are instructed to admonish "Masters or Dames" of whom servants had complained of tyrannical and cruel abuse. Upon the second complaint the laborer was to be protected by the officers until the Sessions Court met to consider his case. (No. 21) Lent by Town of North Hempstead.

UNFAIR COMPETITION PROTESTED. October 13, 1675. Coopers of South and East Hampton, Long Island, petition for protection against unfair competition from Boston coopers who came in for winter season. Early example in the colony of an effort of artificers to confine the work of a particular trade to local craftsmen. N. Y. Colonial Manuscripts, v. 24, p. 164. (No. 22) From the State Library, Albany.

LANSINGBURGH CARPENTERS ORGANIZE. June 19, 1790. Rules and regulations formulated "for the good government of themselves, and the benefit of their employers." In addition to regulating wages, they provided for help in cases of unemployment. Early example of labor union in New York State. (No. 23) From the State Library, Albany.

A LAW INCORPORATING ALBANY MECHANICS SOCIETY. March 6, 1801. The Society was founded "for the laudable purposes of protecting and supporting such of their brethren as by sickness or accident may stand in need of assistance and of relieving the widows and orphans of those who may die in indigent circumstances; and also of providing the means of instruction for their children." Membership was open to mechanics or tradesmen resident within the City of Albany or its vicinity. Original Laws of 1801, Chapter 15. First page shown. (No. 24) From the State Library, Albany.

GENERAL REGISTER OF ALBANY MECHANICS SOCIETY. 1801. This register shows: Philip Hooker, the noted architect, as a carpenter; Jeremiah Van Rensselaer, a painter; gold and silversmiths, bookbinders, printers, umbrella makers, cabinet makers, etc. (No. 25) From the State Library, Albany.

BUILDING CONTRACT FOR ARSENAL. April 29, 1799. Contract between John Jay, Governor, and Philip Hooker and Elisha Putnam, builders, for constructing the arsenal in Albany; with design by Philip Hooker. In State Comptroller's Records. (No. 26) From the State Library, Albany.

LABOR'S OPPORTUNITY FOR SELF-DEVELOPMENT. 1835. Mechanics and Labourers Association of Troy and Albia addressed by Martin I. Townsend on their opportunities for self-development and the dignity of labor and the mechanical arts. The "intelligent operative mechanic" has contributed immeasurably to our progress in railroads, steamboats, printing-presses, and manufactures. (No. 27) From the State Library, Albany.

UTICA MECHANICS ASSOCIATION DIPLOMA. February 15, 1858. Awarded for the best harness, trunks, and saddles. Represents the promotion of and pride in the quality of American native products. (No. 28) From the State Library, Albany.

UNEMPLOYMENT INSURANCE LAW. April 25, 1935. Called by Governor Lehman "the most enlightened piece of social legislation enacted in this State in many decades." Original Law with memorandum of approval by the Governor. (No. 29) From the State Library, Albany.

NEW YORK ANTIDISCRIMINATION LAW. March 12, 1945. This is the first general law in the United States against discrimination in employment: "against persons because of race, creed, color, or national origin." Original Laws of 1945, Chapter 118. (No. 30) From the Secretary of State.

CAR II. LIBERTY UNDER LAW

CASE 1. PERSONAL LIBERTY

INDIAN SLAVERY ABOLISHED. December 5, 1679. By order of the New York Executive Council, "all Indyans here are free and not Slaves, nor can bee forc'd to bee servants." N. Y. Colonial Manuscripts, v. 28, p. 173. (No. 31) From the State Library, Albany.

DANIEL D. TOMPKINS "ON SLAVERY." 1793. This essay advocating the cause of liberty for all men was written when young Tompkins, later to become governor of New York, was a student at Columbia College. (No. 32) From the State Library, Albany.

GRADUAL ABOLITION OF NEGRO SLAVERY IN NEW YORK. March 29, 1799. This law provided that after July 4, 1799, every child born of slave parents in New York State should be free. Original Laws of 1799, Chapter 62. (No. 33) From the State Library, Albany.

NEW YORK SUPPORTS CHILDREN OF NEGRO SLAVES UNDER GRADUAL ABOLITION LAW. January 1, 1804. Southfield Town, Richmond County (Staten Island) submits accounts for maintenance of children of negro slaves born after July 4, 1799. (No. 34) Lent by Staten Island Historical Society, New York City.

ORIGINAL DRAFT BY ABRAHAM LINCOLN OF EMANCIPATION PROCLAMATION. September 22, 1862. Original manuscript draft of first proclamation providing for freedom of negro slaves. The document is in Lincoln's own handwriting. Several of the corrections are in Seward's handwriting. Contributed by Lincoln to the Albany Army Relief Bazaar to be sold at auction and the proceeds used for care of wounded soldiers. Bought for $1,000 by the New York State Legislature for the New York State Library. (No. 35) From the State Library, Albany.

PLEDGE OF ALLEGIANCE TO THE FLAG. 1892. Original draft written in 1892, by Francis Bellamy of Rochester, New York. The Pledge has since been revised to include the words "United States of America." It is used by all schools and patriotic groups throughout the country. Document shown in Bellamy's own handwriting. (No. 36) Lent by David Bellamy, Rochester, New York.

FIRST PRINTING OF THE PLEDGE OF ALLEGIANCE TO THE FLAG. 1892. Program containing first printing of the Pledge. The year 1892 marked the 400th Anniversary of the discovery of America by Columbus in 1492. Francis Bellamy wrote the Pledge for use in the Columbus Day celebrations of that year. (No. 37) From the State Library, Albany.

CASE 2. SUFFRAGE AND PROPERTY RIGHTS

NEW YORK'S THIRD STATE CONSTITUTION. 1846. This Constitution abolished all remnants of feudalism and oligarchical government. All white men 21 years of age or older could now vote whether they owned property or not, confirming the amendment of 1826, to the Constitution of 1821. This Constitution became a model for others. It was copied by Wisconsin and several other midwestern states. (No. 38) From the State Library, Albany.

THE LILY, "DEVOTED TO THE INTERESTS OF WOMEN." 1849. Amelia Bloomer, pioneer woman journalist and leader in the Woman's Rights movement, began publication of this magazine, The Lily, in 1849, in Seneca Falls, New York, the birthplace of the Woman's Rights movement in 1848. The State Library has her personal copies of volumes 1 to 6. Exhibited here are: the titlepage of volume 1, Mrs. Bloomer's story of the enterprise in her own handwriting, and her picture, showing her in the original costume that she designed. This costume thus got the name "Bloomer." (No. 39) From the State Library, Albany.

POLITICAL EQUALITY CLUB OF CATTARAUGUS COUNTY. Minute Book, 1891-1896. An early woman's suffrage club, showing the widespread interest in the movement for woman's rights in this State. Little Valley, Salamanca, Randolph and Conewango are represented in the membership, which included some men. (No. 40) From the State Library, Albany.

SUSAN B. ANTHONY GETS STATE POST. December 14, 1892. Susan B. Anthony, famous leader in the Woman's Rights movement, accepts appointment by Governor Roswell P. Flower to the Board of Managers of the State Industrial School at Rochester. This is her first official position in any governmental agency; she was at the time 72 years old. She thanks the Governor "in the name of all women—especially the few who, with me for the last forty years, have been asking of the government equality of rights—civil and political—for our half of the people." (No. 41) From the State Library, Albany.

"VOTES FOR WOMEN" PILGRIMAGE. 1912. "Votes for Women" pilgrims walk all the way from New York City to carry this message of greeting to the Governor-elect William Sulzer on his arrival at the Capitol in Albany. The earnestness of these suffragettes is realized by their determination to make the pilgrimage afoot despite the wintry December weather. (No. 42) From the State Library, Albany.

WOMAN'S SUFFRAGE URGED BY DR. MARY E. WALKER. 1915. Dr. Mary E. Walker, another distinguished leader in the cause of woman's rights, delivers her speech before the Suffrage Commitee of New York State Constitutional Convention of 1915, in Albany. A measure to permit women to vote was presented to every New York State Legislature from 1854 to 1917. The goal was finally achieved by an amendment to the State Constitution in 1917. (No. 43) From the State Library, Albany.

NEW YORK ASSEMBLY SEEKS PROTECTION OF PROPERTY RIGHTS. October 24, 1700. Bill passed to void the New York City ordinance levying an impost duty on flour and biscuit brought into the city. Assembly calls ordinance an infringement and destruction of the "Libertys propertys and inheritance" of His Majesty's subjects. Bill failed of approval by Governor and Council. The official seal of New York City still bears two symbolic flour barrels. (No. 44) From the State Library, Albany.

CASE 3. MILITARY SECURITY

ALBANY PLAN OF UNION. 1754. Drawn up by Benjamin Franklin at the Albany Congress in 1754. This Congress met in Albany to plan for better defense of the colonies by cooperative action against menace of the French and Indians. The Plan provided for a representative council to make general laws and for raising and levying taxes to defray the cost of defense. Although it failed of adoption, it was the most important attempt at federated action in the colonies prior to the Revolution. Sir William Johnson Papers, v. 1, p. 127-ff. (No. 45) From the State Library, Albany.

"FRIENDS OF LIBERTY." January 8, 1776. The Westchester County Committee of Safety writes from White Plains to assure the New York Provincial Committee of Safety of its loyal support. N. Y. Provincial Congress Archives, v. 25. (No. 46) From the State Library, Albany.

CANNON BORROWED BY NEW YORK PATRIOTS. July 27, 1776. John Jay secures from Connecticut the loan of 20 cannon. Copy of the minutes of the meeting of the Connecticut Governor and Council of Safety with Governor Trumbull's signature of approval. Subjoined is Connecticut Governor Trumbull's pass to permit Jay, "a gentleman friendly to the United States," to travel in Connecticut on the following day, which was a Sunday. (No. 47) From Washington's Headquarters, Newburgh.

GENERAL BURGOYNE SURRENDERS AFTER DECISIVE DEFEAT IN BATTLE OF SARATOGA. October 17, 1777. Orderly book of one of General Burgoyne's officers, with terms of surrender signed October 17, 1777, after the decisive defeat of the British at Saratoga. This defeat of the British changed their entire plan of campaign to subdue the colonies. It was one of the decisive battles of history, because the Americans won for their cause both European recognition and support. French military and naval aid were promised and financial assistance was immediately forthcoming. England had to wage a world war. The successful outcome of the Revolutionary War for the United States was thereby assured. (No. 48) From the State Library, Albany.

"PLAN OF THE POSITION WHICH THE ARMY UNDER LT. GENL. BURGOINE TOOK AT SARATOGA ON THE 10TH OF SEPTEMBER 1777 AND IN WHICH IT REMAINED TILL THE CONVENTION WAS SIGNED." (No. 49) From the State Library, Albany.

PAPERS FOUND ON BRITISH SPY MAJOR ANDRÉ. Papers found in the boots of Major John André, the British spy, during the Revolutionary War. Major André was captured near Tarrytown by the Americans while returning from his visit to General Benedict Arnold, Commander at West Point. André's plight invoked the sympathies of the Americans, even those of General Washington, but he was hanged as a reprisal for the previous similar execution of the American patriot, Captain Nathan Hale, by the British. Documents shown are: (1) description of the works at West Point, in Arnold's handwriting; (2) return of ordnance in the various forts, batteries, etc. at West Point and its dependencies, September 5, 1780. (No. 50) From the State Library, Albany.

GENERAL GEORGE WASHINGTON RECEIVES TRIUMPHAL WELCOME IN NEW YORK CITY AT THE CLOSE OF THE WAR FOR INDEPENDENCE. 1783. Rare broadside announcing order for triumphal entry of Washington and his army into New York City. (No. 51) From the State Library, Albany.

NEW YORK STATE'S FIRST GOVERNOR GEORGE CLINTON HONORED. 1783. General Washington congratulates Governor George Clinton on the achievement of peace at victorious conclusion of the Revolutionary War. A draft of Clinton's reply returning the compliment is on the other side. (No. 52) From the State Library, Albany.

PRESIDENT WASHINGTON'S HOUSEHOLD EXPENSES. 1789. Tabulated accounts of Washington's household expenses for 1789, the first year of his Presidency, when he resided in New York City, then the nation's capital. All of the entries are in Washington's own handwriting. (No. 53) From the State Library, Albany.

BATTLE OF PLATTSBURG. September, 1814. Decisive naval victory achieved in New York State, in the War of 1812. This War secured for the United States the recognition of freedom of the seas and security for all who sailed or traded under her Flag. (No. 54) From the State Library, Albany.

NEW YORK'S RATIFICATION OF THE FEDERAL CONSTITUTION AT THE POUGHKEEPSIE CONVENTION. June-July, 1788. Journal of Proceedings. New York, after much political agitation and controversy finally ratified the Federal Constitution, in the convention held at Poughkeepsie. The stormy sessions of the convention were marked by acrimonious debate. The final pages bear the signatures of the delegates. (No. 55) From the State Library, Albany.

THE FEDERALIST. New York, 1788. This famous series of political essays argued the ratification of the Federal Constitution in New York. They were written by Alexander Hamilton, John Jay, both of New York, and James Madison, of Virginia; and they appeared serially in New York City newspapers. This book is the first collected edition of the essays. The gift of the United States to the world's political development was the governmental device and political institution of the federal state. The Federalist forms the textbook of this new principle of government. (No. 56) From the State Library, Albany.

DIE CONSTITUTIE. Albany, 1788. Federal Constitution, translated for the German population by the Reverend Lambertus de Ronde, and published by order of the Federal Committee in the city of Albany by Charles R. Webster. De Ronde was a minister in New York City and later in Schaghticoke. There were many Germans, especially Palatines, among the early settlers in the Albany area. (No. 57) From the State Library, Albany.

THE CONSTITUTION, IN FRENCH. Paris, 1792. Printed in French edition of the Federalist. The French had cooperated in the struggle for freedom in America and were keenly interested to read in their own language the basic document establishing our federal government. (No. 58) From the State Library, Albany.

WASHINGTON'S FAREWELL ADDRESS. 1797. First draft, in Washington's own handwriting. On leaving the Presidency Washington declared that the "common Government . . . being free in its principle—being founded in our own choice—being intended as the guardian of our common rights . . . and wisely containing within itself a provision for its own amendment . . . seems to promise everything that can be expected from such an institution;—and if supported by wise Councils—by virtuous conduct—and by mutual and friendly allowances, must approach as near to perfection as any human work can aspire, and nearer than any which the annals of mankind have recorded." Note the care with which Washington made changes in the manuscript. He was trained as a surveyor, and hence used a ruler in making neat corrections. This manuscript lent by the New York State Library to the National Freedom Train was exhibited in every state in the Union. (No. 59) From the State Library, Albany.

NEW YORK RATIFIES THE FEDERAL CONSTITUTION. 1788. Engrossed copy of the Constitution on parchment, signed by Governor George Clinton as president of the Ratification Convention, held at Poughkeepsie, June-July 1788. First and last pages shown. A "no third term" proposition "That no Person shall be eligible to the Office of President of the United States a third Time," which was not incorporated into the Bill of Rights, has since been adopted by the 80th Congress and presented to the several states for approval as the 22nd Amendment to the Constitution. (No. 60) From the State Library, Albany.

POUGHKEEPSIE CONVENTION TO RATIFY THE FEDERAL CONSTITUTION. July 26, 1788. Photograph of mural by Gerald Foster in the Poughkeepsie post office.

CAR III. Freedom of Self-development

CASE 1. Mobility

JEWISH EMIGRATION TO NEW NETHERLAND APPROVED. March 13, 1656. Directors of Dutch West India Company inform Governor Peter Stuyvesant that Jews are allowed to settle in New Netherland "and there to enjoy the same liberty that is granted them in this country [Holland] . . . with respect to civil and political liberties." Jews came from Holland, Brazil and elsewhere. (Document is in the Dutch language.) N. Y. Colonial Manuscripts, v. 12, p. 36. (No. 61) From the State Library, Albany.

CANALS DECLARED ESSENTIAL TO NEW YORK STATE'S DEVELOPMENT. February 20, 1816. New York City Common Council memorializes the State Legislature on its concern over the "great and important Canal question." Canal system to form a "bond of union," and afford opportunity for population to move into the interior of the country and develop its vast resources. Assembly Papers, v. 43, p. 153. (No. 62) From the State Library, Albany.

MAP OF THE WESTERN PART OF THE STATE OF NEW YORK, SHOWING THE ROUTE OF A PROPOSED CANAL FROM LAKE ERIE TO HUDSON RIVER. COMPILED BY JOHN H. EDDY. 1811. Plans for a canal had been discussed and developed since the 1790's. Work on the first section of the Erie Canal was started at Rome on July 4, 1817. The whole canal, from Albany to Buffalo, was opened in 1825. (No. 63) From the State Library, Albany.

ERIE CANAL AFFORDS EMIGRANTS EASY TRANSPORTATION TO THE WEST. 1828. Passenger list of canal boat filed with the State Comptroller's records. Traffic on the canal was extensive. Countless similar passenger lists and registrations of boats make up these records. The document shows the vital importance of the Canal in hastening western movement and settlement. (No. 64) From the State Library, Albany.

MOHAWK AND HUDSON RAILROAD CHARTERED. April 17, 1826. The first railroad in New York State began operation in 1831. It was the first link in the present vast New York Central System. Original Laws of 1826, Chapter 253. (No. 65) From the State Library, Albany.

"THE FIRST LOCOMOTIVE AND TRAIN OF PASSENGER CARS EVER RUN IN THE STATE OF NEW YORK." Reproduction of cut-out by William H. Brown, a passenger on its first excursion trip in 1831. (No. 66) From the State Library, Albany.

AMERICANS AID POLISH REFUGEES IN THEIR STRUGGLE FOR INDEPENDENCE. 1831-1832. Correspondence of the Polish-American Committee in Paris with General LaFayette, distributing agent in Paris for funds raised in New York State to aid Polish refugees in Prussia. Shown are: letters of A. B. Johnson, secretary of the Committee, and of the West Point Military Academy Cadet Corps which contributed to the fund; and letter of LaFayette to James Fenimore Cooper, who took Samuel Gridley Howe's place as chairman during the latter's imprisonment in Germany for his activities in the movement. (No. 67) From the State Library, Albany.

AMERICA'S SYMBOL OF FREEDOM—THE STATUE OF LIBERTY. "The New Colossus," original manuscript of the poem, written in 1883, by Emma Lazarus, New York Jewess, inscribed on the base of the Statue of Liberty, welcoming the oppressed peoples of the world to our shores. The Statue, the symbol of America, was given by the people of France, and unveiled in 1886, on its present site in New York Harbor. (No. 67A) Lent by the American-Jewish Historical Society, New York.

CASE 2. Education

SCHOOLMASTER FOR ALBANY. May 16, 1670. English Colonial Governor Lovelace reappointed Jan Jurians Beecker to teach the youth "to read and to wryte." N. Y. Council Minutes, v. 2, p. 536. (No. 68) From the State Library, Albany.

"ON GENERAL DIFFUSION OF KNOWLEDGE." 1793. Only thus can our liberty be safeguarded, wrote Daniel D. Tompkins, in 1793, when a student at Columbia College. He later became Governor of the State.(No. 69) From the State Library, Albany.

EDUCATIONAL OPPORTUNITY FOR THE POOR. 1804. Education for children of indigent citizens in New York State guaranteed by act of the Legislature. Assembly Papers, v. 42, p. 148. (No. 70) From the State Library, Albany.

FREE SCHOOLS PUBLICLY SUPPORTED. February 25, 1805. Urged by DeWitt Clinton and other New Yorkers as important in preserving an enlightened government. First page of document shown. Assembly Papers, v. 42, p. 103. (No. 71) From the State Library, Albany.

NEW YORK PROVIDES FOR EDUCATION OF CHILDREN OF FRENCH IMMIGRANTS. 1810. Economical School in New York City, incorporated 1810, asks January 6, 1821 for additional state funds. Assembly Papers, v. 42, p. 520. (No. 72) From the State Library, Albany.

COLUMBIA COLLEGE RECEIVES ATTENTION OF THOMAS JEFFERSON. October 6, 1823. In letter to John Griscom, professor of chemistry and natural philosophy, Jefferson asks for copy of regulations to aid in the preparation of a "code of regulations for the administration and discipline" of the University of Virginia, soon to be opened. "Enlighten the people generally," Jefferson wrote in 1816, "and tyranny and oppression of both mind and body will vanish like evil spirits at the dawn of day." (No. 73) From Washington's Headquarters, Newburgh.

CORNELL UNIVERSITY CHARTERED BY NEW YORK STATE LEGISLATURE. April 27, 1865. Leading object "to teach such branches of learning as are related to agriculture and the mechanic arts, including military tactics, in order to promote the liberal and practical education of the industrial classes in the several pursuits and professions in life." A land grant college, it was to receive income from the sale of lands donated to New York State by the Federal Government under the First Morrill Act, July 2, 1862. Preference was to be given (other qualifications being equal) to the sons of those who had died in Military or Naval service of the United States. (No. 74) From the State Library, Albany.

NO DISCRIMINATION IN EDUCATIONAL OPPORTUNITY. April 3, 1948. Admission to post-secondary educational institutions under New York State Board of Regents to be denied no one on account of race, color, religion, creed, or national origin. Original Laws of 1948, Chapter 753. (No. 75) From Secretary of State.

CASE 3. Science

NEW YORK'S FIRST AGRICULTURAL SOCIETY. 1791. Society for Promotion of Agriculture, Arts and Manufactures, organized in 1791, incorporated in 1793, was the first agricultural society in New York State and the fifth in the country. Its founders included some of the foremost citizens of the State. The purposes and activities of the Society were many; among them was the stressing of the value of the experimental method to improve agriculture. Original Laws of 1793. (No. 76) From the State Library, Albany.

SCIENCE TEACHING IN NEW YORK STATE APPROVED. December 7, 1788. Regents of University of the State of New York express in their report to the Legislature their satisfaction with the progress and development of scientific studies in Columbia College and the several academies under their jurisdiction. Assembly Papers, v. 43, p. 13. (No. 77) From the State Library, Albany.

RENSSELAER POLYTECHNIC INSTITUTE, TROY. First scientific school established in The United States, opened in 1825. Founded by Stephen Van Rensselaer to instruct youth "in the application of science to the common purposes of life." On exhibit are: (1) Constitution submitted November 5, 1824 by Stephen Van Rensselaer in letter to the Reverend Samuel Blatchford, first president; (2) letter of Stephen Van Rensselaer to Samuel Blatchford, February 11, 1825, submitting (3) supplementary By-laws; (4) Catalogue of 1845, setting forth aims of founder. (No. 78) From the State Library, Albany.

CASE 4. STATE SERVICE

NEW YORK'S CIVIL SERVICE LAW. May 4, 1883. New York was the first state to place a civil service law on its statute books. Theodore Roosevelt headed the Committee of the Assembly that introduced the bill, and it became a law upon the signature of Governor Grover Cleveland. The New York Civil Service Reform Association, first civil service reform organization in the country and now oldest civic reform body of any kind in the nation, had its beginnings in New York City in 1878. (No. 79) From the State Library, Albany.

CARL SCHURZ OPPOSES CHANGES IN NEW YORK'S CIVIL SERVICE LAW. 1897. Carl Schurz was president of National Civil Service Reform League, 1892-1900; and he also served as president of New York Civil Service Reform Association, 1893-1906. As a young student in Germany he took part in the Liberal Revolutionary Movement of 1848-9 and emigrated to escape the persecutions that followed. He served as general in the Union Army during the Civil War. His interests and leadership were given to the development of American cultural life and the improvement of political morality. (No. 80) From the State Library, Albany.

GOVERNOR FRANKLIN D. ROOSEVELT ADVOCATES OPEN COMPETITIVE CIVIL SERVICE EXAMINATIONS. September, 1931. (No. 81) From the State Library, Albany.

CONSTITUTION MAKERS. 1821. Roll of delegates to convention which framed New York Constitution of 1821. Note the recording of occupations and other personal information about the delegates. (No. 82) From the State Library, Albany.

CONSTITUTION MAKERS. 1846. Roll of delegates to convention which framed New York Constitution of 1846, the "People's Constitution." Note the recording of occupations and other personal information about the delegates. (No. 83) From the State Library, Albany.

The New York State Freedom Train, a library on wheels, visits the principal communities of the State, (left) a teacher explains one of the documents to her class; (above) a family studies the documents together.